the mayne inheritance

Rosamond Siemon was born in Boonah, Queensland, in 1921. She was educated at St Margaret's, and obtained a Ph.D. in history from the University of Queensland. She served in the Women's Auxiliary Australian Air Force, and was a current affairs broadcaster with ABC Radio and a Radio Australia correspondent 1955–72. She served on the Oriental Studies Society, and the Co-ordinating Committee for Overseas Students in Queensland and was the Singapore government's student liaison officer in Queensland. From 1972–81, she was the Alumni officer at the University of Queensland, and is an elected member of the Convocation of the University of Queensland. She lives in Brisbane.

the mayne inheritance

a gothic tale of murder, madness and scandal across the generations

rosamond siemon

UQP

First published 1997 by University of Queensland Press
Box 6042, St Lucia, Queensland 4067 Australia
www.uqp.com.au

Paperback edition 1998, reprinted three times
New paperback edition 1999, reprinted 2000 (twice)
New edition 2001, reprinted 2002 (twice)
New edition 2003, reprinted 2005, 2008, 2010, 2012, 2017, 2018, 2019, 2020, 2022, 2023, 2025

Typeset by University of Queensland Press
Printed in Australia by McPherson's Printing Group

Sponsored by the Queensland Office of Arts and Cultural Development.

Cataloguing in Publication Data
National Library of Australia

Siemon, Rosamond.
The Mayne Inheritance.

1. Mayne family. 2. Politicians — Queensland — Brisbane — Biography. 3. Irish — Queensland — Brisbane — Biography. 4. Hospital administrators — Queensland — Brisbane — Biography. 5. Brisbane (Qld.) — Biography. I. Title.

994.31030922

ISBN 978 0 7022 3422 4

MIX
Paper | Supporting responsible forestry
FSC® C001695

For my mother Annie Sarah Nunn
whose enthusiasm for the study of history
inspired my similar interest.

Contents

Acknowledgments *ix*
Preface *xi*
Mayne Family Chart *xv*

Chapter 1 A Profitable Murder *1*
Chapter 2 Ireland to Australia *15*
Chapter 3 Law Courts & Land Deals *34*
Chapter 4 Consolidating an Empire *49*
Chapter 5 In and Out of Council *72*
Chapter 6 Life in Queen Street *83*
Chapter 7 Crisis After Crisis *97*
Chapter 8 Out of the Ashes *112*
Chapter 9 A Family Ostracised *132*

Chapter 10 The Tobita Murder and Its Aftermath *154*
Chapter 11 The Burden of Inheritance *169*
Chapter 12 Maynes and the University of Queensland *182*

Epilogue *204*
Sources *212*

Preface

I have known of the Mayne family since I was a child. My knowledge probably dates from the late 1920s when Mary Emelia and James Mayne, the last of the family, donated the money to buy the St Lucia site for the University of Queensland. At that time most of the specious stories which maligned the family resurfaced. In their gruesome variety they still circulate.

If it seems surprising knowledge for a family who lived deep in the mountain-rimmed Fassifern Valley, I can only imagine that, as some of my family regularly climbed those rugged mountains with a group of Brisbane-based bushwalkers, we heard the stories around the nightly campfire. Among the group were several amateur historians such as Danny O'Brien, Romeo Lahey and Doug Jolly.

When, for a few short years before World War 2, I lived by the river at Hill End in Brisbane, I saw where the Mayne family lived. We could see the house, "Moorlands", from the Toowong ferry. Locals frequently pointed across the river and said conspiratorily, "That's a bad place." Fate kept the Maynes forever in my sight. I married into a family who were their neighbours. The Siemons' "Ravensfield" was separated from "Moorlands" by a small creek and a rough track called Patrick Lane. No Siemon child was ever allowed to cross the shallow creek. "Moorlands" was out of bounds, regarded as an "evil place". My mother-in-law, a gentle, charitable Christian lady, never defined that term. Her knowledge of the Maynes went back many years. Before her marriage she had lived in "Rocklily", high on the cliff above the river and overlooking "Moorlands". Living the sheltered life of girls of her day, she had accepted without question that the Maynes were not respectable people.

In 1972 I learned of the Maynes' three major bequests to the University of Queensland when I joined the staff as Alumni Officer. What was a big surprise was how much mystery surrounded this family, which must be one of the greatest, if not *the* greatest benefactor of the University of Queensland and the State's community. When looking for material for a short informative article on them, I came across a list of items that had graced their home and which had come to the University after Mary Emelia Mayne died. With some difficulty, I located them all. They were excellent pieces of nineteenth-century workmanship, and, with the exception of the magnificent cedar table, once used as the Senate table, but which a staff member had later purchased, they were put on display at an "EXPO UNI".

In subsequent years I often wondered about the family. Could the people who had been so generous to their community have been as bad as the stories suggest? It became important to me to know the truth. In 1993, after delivering my PhD thesis to the examiners, I countered the withdrawal symptoms which accompanied the long wait for assessment by delving into the Mayne family history. There I was to learn that one of the last people, supposedly involved in this family tragedy, who had died an unnatural death, had at one time been employed by my father-in-law. There was no way I could abandon this story.

Long research into a family history inevitably draws one into their life. To me they are no longer cardboard figures based on facts and footnotes. Rightly or wrongly I believe that they reveal a personality which one can understand just as one has an intuitive understanding of one's own child. In this account I have given the facts, but the family has become very real to me. It cries out for understanding, so I have taken a little licence and added a dimension that, I hope, gives their tragedy a more human face.

We know that the Maynes suffered the stark reality of the long reach of the sins of the fathers. We do not know how far back in time the first culprit-father existed. Perhaps we should be questioning why communities take their revenge and persecute the children who never asked for the ignominy they inherited.

THE MAYNE FAMILY

BORN	MARRIED	DIED	CAUSE	BURIED
PATRICK 1824 Cookstown Ireland	9.4.1849	17.8.1865 Queen St	Unknown	Paddington
Mary (*née* McIntosh) 17.8.1821 Ennis Clare Ireland	9.4.1849	4.9.1889 Moorlands Villa	Heart Failure	Toowong
Mary Kelly (Mary's mother. *née* Nash. 1 McIntosh, 2 Kelly.) 1800 Ireland	twice	24.3.1865 Bowen Hills	Unknown	Paddington
Ann Mayne (Patrick's sister) 1829 Cookstown Ireland	—	4.7.1905 Moorlands	Cirrhosis	Toowong
<u>CHILDREN</u> Rosanna 30.1.1850 Queen St Brisbane	—	7.3.1934 All Hallows' Convent	Senile Decay	Nudgee
Isaac Patrick 14.1.1852 Queen St	—	31.1.1905 Bayview Asylum, Sydney	Suicide	Toowong
Evelina Selina 19.10.1853 Queen St	—	8.11.1854 Queen St	Unknown	Paddington
William McIntosh 17.5.1856 Queen St	—	16.8.1921 Moorlands	Heart Failure	Toowong
Mary Emelia 31.12.1858 Queen St	—	12.8.1940 Moorlands	Senile Decay Heart Failure	Toowong
James O'Neil 21.1.1861 Queen St	—	31.1.1939 Moorlands	Cerebral oedema Hyptertension Arterio-sclerosis	Toowong

<u>NOTES:</u>

1. For both Patrick and Mary Mayne the immigration records indicate a birth date which differs from that on their marriage certificate and on the family tomb.
2. Although Patrick and Evelina were both buried at Paddington and their headstone is still there, their name appears on the family tomb at Toowong. Rosanna's name is not on the tomb.
3. Paddington Cemetery was sometimes referred to as Milton Cemetery.

1

A Profitable Murder

HAD it not been for a murder and robbery on Sunday, 26 March 1848, the University of Queensland would not be sited at St Lucia. It would most likely have occupied a more cramped campus at Gilchrist Avenue, Victoria Park, adjoining the Brisbane General Hospital. An innocent man was hanged for the crime. The murderer confessed in August, 1865. This is not a pleasant story. It is as macabre as a Greek Tragedy. Its ghastly consequences fell on the shoulders of others, not least on the murderer's youngest son and daughter who fought hard to redeem their family name and honour. A hostile community made sure they failed in this, but their generosity which benefited that community shows that an evil act can sometimes lead to good consequences.

Ever since that deathbed confession there has been speculation about the identity of the victim, and the many fanciful stories which have been repeated about the murderer and the crime. Such stories still abound. It is important to dispel the myths and reveal the details of the inquest to see what really happened.

On Monday, 27 March 1848, the people of Brisbane town were shocked to learn of an exceptionally brutal murder at Kangaroo Point. The victim was Robert Cox, a sawyer, who a few days before had arrived from the Tweed River area with a friend, Richard Smith. In the pre-dawn hours of Sunday morning he had been stabbed in the right side, the chest, neck and belly by a knife which left wounds an inch wide and three inches deep. The body had been expertly butchered.

An early morning boatman and his family, rowing down the Brisbane River, were horrified to see the legs and loins of a body, well below high-water mark, at the bottom of Rankin's garden at the end of Main Street. At eight o'clock a hastily roused Constable Murphy found the arms and upper torso in grass three metres away. Several local residents, many of them regular customers at the adjoining Bush Inn, at the corner of Main and Holman Streets, were drawn by the commotion and quickly arrived at the scene to join the search for the head. A dog eventually led them to where it was propped between two joists in a nearby unfinished building belonging to Mr Colin

Campbell. When the head was picked up it was still bleeding. Constable Murphy had the body reassembled at the Bush Inn and called the surgeon, Kearsey Cannon. He reported that the abdomen had been cut open with a large knife and the spine divided with an axe or similar instrument. The chest had been opened from top to bottom and on the right side. The cartilages of the ribs had been divided with a strong knife and the head severed in a similar manner to the two parts of the body. Surgeon Cannon added that from the mutilated state of the body it was impossible to say in which manner the deceased was murdered.

From the well in the backyard of the hotel and across the dividing fence to Rankin's garden, where the body was found, the grass was heavily bloodstained. When a helpful bystander descended the well on a ladder he found some of Cox's intestines, a table-knife and three shirts and a towel, all bloodstained. The water in the well and in a bucket at the top was heavily contaminated with blood. Black trackers were called, and James Davis (Duramboi), a former convict who had lived for some years with a tribe of Aborigines and was now a blacksmith at Kangaroo Point, reported that the murder had occurred between the hotel and the fence. From the rapidly growing group of bystanders, a Mr Nosely identified the body as Robert Cox, who had a bed at his house. A butcher from the slaughterhouse, William Lynch, said that Cox had stayed at his house on Friday night. Questioned by Constable Murphy, Lynch appeared agitated, his countenance changed from red to pale. The constable arrested both Nosely and Lynch.

Some hotel patrons, the licensee William Sutton, and his daughter Charlotte Sutton, had seen Cox early on Saturday evening asleep in the bed of the hotel cook, William Fyfe. Many years earlier, Cox and Fyfe had been convicts at Moreton Bay and they were still very close friends. Since coming to Brisbane town, Cox had been steadily drinking to cut out a £4 money order which he had given to the publican at the Bush Inn. Later, at the inquest, a hotel patron, Thomas Gnossill, said in evidence that he had seen Cox and Fyfe together several times in the preceding days and they were "like brothers". Constable Murphy immediately searched Fyfe's room; among his dirty clothes he found a towel marked with blood. In later evidence, Charlotte Sutton mentioned that Fyfe's lips had looked very sore and bleeding, something that Murphy must have noticed. Nevertheless, he promptly arrested Fyfe. Shortly afterwards, the constable took into custody the licensee William Sutton, and William Holt, a hotel resident who had been awake until four in the morning and had heard nothing. The next to be arrested were two mates of the butcher, William Lynch — George Platt and a barely sober John Connell. The latter had spent part of Saturday drunk on the hotel kitchen floor and all of that night drunk on the taproom table.

A grand jury was hastily assembled at Sutton's Hotel to examine the suspects and decide if there was sufficient evidence to send any of them to Sydney to be tried. A key player in the events, the publican, had earlier told Constable Murphy that he thought his cook, Fyfe, was the villain. Now he added that he saw someone who he supposed was Cox in Fyfe's bed at eleven o'clock when he locked up for the night and went to bed. Fyfe was still up at about one o'clock when Sutton was aroused by three customers wanting a drink. They were regular patrons who had been in the hotel earlier in the evening. From her bedroom, Charlotte Sutton recognised the voices as those of three local butchers: William Lynch, George Platt and Patrick Mayne. All three had been drinking at the hotel earlier. Now they went on drinking for some time. They later declared that they saw and heard nothing, except for the snores of John Connell, in a drunken stupor on the taproom table. In evidence, Platt swore that he and Sutton were sober, leaving the inference that Lynch and Mayne were not. If this was so, it is surprising that Patrick Mayne's very plausible evidence was so precise about the time they arrived and left the hotel and the length of time he afterwards spent at his lodgings conversing with his two workmates, Lynch and Platt. According to Mayne, they drank for a short time in the early evening, returned to the hotel at twenty minutes to one on Sunday morning and drank ginger beer and wine until three o'clock, at which time they went to his lodgings and conversed until four o'clock. Miss Charlotte Sutton's evidence put the time of their arrival at about midnight and their leaving about an hour later. Fyfe, the cook, was still up when they left and asked Sutton for a glass of beer, saying: "That fellow Cox has gone." As both the hotel and the back gate had been locked for the night at eleven o'clock, Sutton asked how he went. "He went over the gate at half-past twelve," he was told.

The young son of Sutton's neighbour, Rankin, in whose yard the body was found, said that when answering a call of nature in their backyard during the night, he had seen a tall man in white with a big straw hat standing by his father's fence. He thought it was Mr Sutton, the publican.

Altogether seven people were arrested: Nosely, with whom Cox boarded; the butchers Lynch and Platt; Fyfe, the cook; hotel patrons Holt and Connell, and the publican, Sutton. Unlike the other local residents who patronised the Bush Inn, Patrick Mayne did not appear on Sunday morning to gawp and give advice. He dropped from view until he was called on the third day to give evidence. One by one the arrested men were released. Finally the publican, Sutton, and his cook, Fyfe, were the only two facing the jury. Fyfe was the chief suspect.

Cox's travelling companion, Richard Smith, told the jury that before they came north, Cox had cut and sold to a Tweed boatyard sixteen or seventeen thousand feet of cedar. Although Cox had given a £4 money order to Mr Sutton to be cut out in drinks, Smith believed that since Cox had no intention of returning to the Tweed district, he had with him the money he had received from the sale of the cedar. The amount was never mentioned and the money was never found. The value of cedar at about that time was fourpence halfpenny or fivepence per foot; it seems reasonable to assume that Cox would have sold his cedar for between £300 and £350, a considerable sum of money at that time.

As Cox had been drinking at the Inn for the past four days it is not unreasonable to accept that others may have been told of the money: Nosely and Lynch, at whose houses he had slept; Mayne and Platt; his close friend, Fyfe, and the many other regular drinkers at the Bush Inn. At three o'clock on Saturday afternoon, Charlotte Sutton and some of the customers at the Inn heard the drunken Cox accuse his friend Fyfe of having robbed him. This Fyfe hotly denied, but Charlotte told her father of the argument. The Suttons did not believe Cox had any money, but it was a good story to pass around the bar and would have been heard by the three butchers — Lynch, Platt, and Mayne, who later returned for post-midnight drinks. There were many opportunities for others to learn about the cedar sale and consider Robert Cox to be worth robbing.

Brisbane at that time was a rough frontier town of rough men. The Bush Inn was a rowdy hotel; the day before the murder Constable Beardmore had arrested the publican, Sutton, for drunkenness. Many of the customers were known to have fled to Australia from a deprived and hungry homeland; many others, ex-convicts, carried a ticket-of-leave. The paucity of women in the colony meant that few had any stable home or family life. They lived and worked under conditions where the solace of drinking their hard-earned wages was the only mind-easing outlet they had. A windfall of money could be the start of a new and better life. This was something they dreamed of; for some, it was the reason they were in Australia. They knew very well that the embryonic colony was a land where those who used their wits as well as their brawn were the ones likely to succeed.

As the evidence unfolded, the Chief Constable, William Fitzpatrick, was not of a mind to allow a crime as savage as this to remain unsolved. He seemed determined to secure a verdict against the cook, William Fyfe. Constable Murphy gave evidence that although on Sunday he had found only a towel with blood stains on it in Fyfe's room, the following Wednesday, when he was again directed to search the room and kitchen and take up one of the floorboards, he found a blood-stained child's shoe, a piece of paper, and bloodstains on the floor. In the kitchen oven he found some burnt buttons, and clothing largely burnt to a white ash. Cross-examined by the prisoner Fyfe, Murphy said that he could not swear that all the clothes he saw in the oven were there when he searched the kitchen three days earlier. He also told the jury that when Fyfe was brought from the lock-up to be confronted with this new "evidence", he seemed dumbfounded. With similar honesty, Murphy stated that on Sunday morning, when Fyfe had lifted the severed head by the hair and identified it as his friend Cox, his hand shook and he was much agitated. Murphy thought that was "because of the awfulness of the spectacle".

Fyfe's former employer, Robert Douglas, told the jury

that Fyfe behaved well and was honest, but was sacked because he got drunk when he (Douglas) was absent. Charlotte Sutton also said that Fyfe was a good servant when sober. In addition, nine local people who were up and about and spoke to the cook between dawn and seven o'clock on Sunday morning said that they noticed nothing remarkable about him. His behaviour seemed as usual to the three washerwomen to whom he made early calls to collect his laundry, and to John McGrath, William Holt, John McGarry, James Jennings, Charlotte Sutton, and George Croft. Croft, who had arrived at a quarter to five on Sunday morning to deliver ginger beer to the Bush Inn, said the ashes of the burnt clothes produced in the court could not have been the result of Fyfe burning them in the oven on Sunday morning. When he arrived, the oven was cold; Fyfe was just lighting it. The ash produced for the jury would have needed an oven hot enough to cook a dinner. A fact that attracted little attention was that on Sunday morning both Charlotte Sutton and a local, John McGrath, who called at six o'clock for a light, saw Nosely and Lynch at the front door of the hotel. A full hour before the body was discovered they had come to enquire if Cox, the victim, was there.

Much of the case against Fyfe rested on the fact that before seven o'clock on Sunday morning he asked Charlotte Sutton for a clean shirt as his had not come back from the washerwoman. In addition he had been seen cleaning out his room with a cloth. At first the jury could not agree, but on Thursday brought in a verdict of wilful murder against Fyfe. To the end there was division of opinion about the innocence of Sutton, but nine of the twelve believed the publican innocent and he was freed. On 12 April the cook, William Fyfe, was sent to Sydney where he faced a judge at Central Criminal Court on 5 June 1848.

In Fyfe's signed statement to the jury before he was committed for trial in Sydney he pointed out that all his clothes which were supposed to have been burnt or found in the well were eventually found elsewhere, without bloodstains and intact. Because the murdered Cox had slept in his bed, his room was thought to be the scene of the murder, but on Sunday nothing was found there except a blood-marked sheet and two towels, stained from Fyfe's bleeding lips. The fact was that in the hotel yard a great amount of blood was traced through long grass and over some chips. From Sunday to Wednesday, while Fyfe was in custody, the kitchen had been unguarded and open to anyone, but on that Wednesday when he was taken from the lock-up to the hotel, the Chief Constable had found blood under his bed. Had it been there all the time, it could have been seen on Sunday by Constable Murphy without raising the floorboards. Fyfe added, "It has been stated in evidence against me that I washed and swept my sleeping room on Sunday, which was not usual. Had I seen the blood,I should have washed that first."

Fyfe's statement carried no weight with the jury. However, in the absence of a motive, few Brisbane townsfolk believed he was guilty, and reports in the *Moreton Bay*

Courier and the *Sydney Morning Herald* echoed that uncertainty. Twelve days after Fyfe was committed, a sawyer, John Humphries, voluntarily gave a signed statement to Captain John Wickham in which he said that on the Saturday afternoon before the Cox murder, Fyfe had come to him to borrow a clean shirt as all of his were dirty and with the washerwoman. He lent him a white shirt and Fyfe returned to the Bush Inn. Captain Wickham forwarded this statement to the court in Sydney, but it carried no weight either. This is surprising, as on 15 June, in Sydney, the same circumstantial evidence as that produced in Brisbane caused the trial judge to comment that the circumstantial evidence was remarkable, and he severely censured the Brisbane policemen for their neglect in not taking charge and locking the cook's room at Sutton's hotel.

In Sydney, on 4 July 1848, Fyfe protested his innocence to the end and walked to the gallows with great dignity. A speech he had planned to deliver on the scaffold was taken from him; and, before a crowd of some four thousand people, he suffered broken bones and flesh wounds in a mismanaged hanging before he died.

In August 1865, during his dying days, Alderman Patrick Mayne, butcher, of Queen Street, Brisbane, then aged forty-one, confessed to the crime committed seventeen years ago.

Some intriguing anomalies surrounding the Cox murder

which were obvious in the evidence suggest that several people knew more than they admitted — and that the jury was not very attentive to the finer points of the witnesses' testimony. All the main witnesses seemed to have been uninterested in sleep on that eventful night. At six o'clock on Sunday morning, a full hour before the boatman discovered the murder, John McGrath saw Lynch and Nosely at the Bush Inn looking for Robert Cox; they both knew he had been asleep in Fyfe's bed on Saturday night and was unlikely to return to either of their lodgings to sleep. By Mayne's testimony, his fellow butchers Lynch and Platt had been with him until four o'clock on Sunday morning. Nor did Sutton seem to have needed much sleep. Although unsure of the precise times, he said that he went to bed at eleven o'clock, got up at one o'clock, drank with the three butchers until three o'clock, then talked to his cook. He was up and fully dressed at five o'clock when Croft delivered the ginger beer. When the black-trackers were asked to trace the blood, Sutton refused to allow them into his premises. Young John Rankin based his identification of Sutton on the fact that he saw a tall man wearing white and a big straw hat. Mayne was tall and, like most men in Brisbane town, wore a big straw hat.

Of all those questioned who had been drinking for much of the weekend, Mayne was the only one who was precise about time. There was probably a clock at the hotel, but it is doubtful that the twenty-three year old employee from the slaughterhouse owned a timepiece which enabled him to state that they talked at his lodgings until four in the morning. He was living very close to the hotel, yet on Sunday morning he was the only one of the group who did not gather with the many locals at the scene of the crime. He was also the only man closely involved with the events of the night before who was not arrested. It is not beyond the realms of possibility that the three butchers — Mayne, Lynch and Platt — believing that Cox had money and that, together with Fyfe, was drunk and asleep, decided to come back to the hotel after midnight and gain access to the cook's bedroom for a spot of easy robbery. When they discovered Cox had gone from the hotel, there may have been hope that a few drinks with the publican would elicit his whereabouts. It also seems reasonable to speculate that when the drunken Cox left Fyfe's bed, he got little further than the hotel backyard before collapsing in a drunken stupor. In that state and in that place he was murdered.

George Croft, a nearby Kangaroo Point resident, heard cries in the night. Those sleeping in the hotel heard nothing and declared that had any noise been made downstairs it would have been heard throughout the building. Had any one of the three butchers who lived and worked near the hotel wanted to implicate the suspect further and divert suspicion from himself, he had ready access to blood at the slaughterhouse, with which to stain the clothes and floor of the cook's bedroom during the absence in the lock-up of both Fyfe and Sutton. Only one of the butchers, Patrick Mayne, was not in the lock-up. No questions were asked as to how, three days after the cook's room had been searched, Chief Constable William Fitzpatrick went back to the deserted room and was able to find bloodstains on the floor and on linen, and in the kitchen the remains of burnt clothes in the oven. No one asked who else might have put them there, or why.

The murder had to have been committed after midnight. The carving up of the body in the manner of a slaughtered beast suggests the murderer was a trained butcher. It is difficult to imagine that Mayne could have perpetrated such a time-consuming crime and been at the hotel during the hours he stated. It seems more reasonable to accept the times given by the only certain sober witness, Charlotte Sutton, who said the three butchers arrived at about midnight and left an hour later. Her stated times make feasible Patrick Mayne's deathbed confession to the murder of Robert Cox.

Nine months after Fyfe was executed, Mayne, now twenty-four, married Mary McIntosh. A few months later he produced the equivalent of five or six years' wages, sufficient money to purchase the shop and business goodwill of the Queen Street butcher James Newbould, then purchase stock and equipment and begin trading.

2

Ireland to Australia

FROM his early years Patrick Mayne knew what he wanted — to break out of his past into a better future. It was so when he fled the unrelieved deprivation of his youth in Ireland, and equally so as he lay dying at his Brisbane home and contemplated the terrors of the hereafter. Between his youth and his premature death is a life that was brutal, spectacular and tragic. No one can say what awfulness in the child's life directed the actions of the man.

Life for the Maynes in County Tyrone was harsh in the extreme. Patrick and his siblings were orphaned years before the Irish famine of 1846, but even then Ireland was a sad and impoverished place for its poorer classes. Three-quarters of the population were Roman Catholics, the majority either labourers or tenant farmers who held land on short leases without security of tenure or protection against increases in rent if they improved their holdings. Agents managing estates for absentee landlords had no social responsibility and were concerned only with extorting the utmost profit from the land. As prices rose after the Napoleonic wars it became profitable to subdivide estates into smaller holdings, often less than ten acres, to increase rent rolls. Landlords were not required to provide farm buildings, or even cottages; a self-erected miserable shack was all that many farmers could manage. Their standard of living was miserably low. The crop, mostly potatoes, constituted the family food. Milk or butter were luxuries rarely seen. Any small grain crop, or perhaps a cow or pig, often had to be sold to pay rent or tithes, which were exacted regularly.

One of life's few consolations was the marriage bed. The little shacks were filled with undernourished children: more mouths to feed and no hope of future work for most of them. Isaac Mayne and his wife Rose, *née* Mullen, were caught in this subsistence trap at Cookstown. They produced at least five living children: Patrick (b. 1824), James (date of birth unknown), Annie (born 1829), Rosa (date of birth unknown), and Eliza (date of birth unknown). Both parents were dead before Patrick turned seventeen; with minimal education he had been labouring wherever he could find work. Ireland's poor were abused by the system, and either directly or indirectly, so were the children. This is reflected in colonial records showing the high incidence of crime and difficulties with authority among the nineteenth-century Irish who were sent, or fled to the colonies. During the first forty poverty-stricken years of the nineteenth century, Ireland's population had doubled to 8,200,000; by 1840 people were being encouraged to migrate to reduce the large numbers of uneconomic land holdings. For those who made the decision to leave, the choice was usually to sail for Canada or America, but by the time the impatient Patrick decided he was old enough to go, Australia, too, was calling for artisans and labourers.

To meet that need, Sydney entrepreneurs were quickly active with Bounty ships. They contracted to bring to Port Jackson strong, healthy young workers for whom they were paid a bounty of £19 a head. The Bounty rules encouraged strict screening for selected migrants. It was cash on delivery and since the promoters were not paid for any who died en route or proved to be puny, diseased, or otherwise unfit for work, they tried to ensure a reasonable standard of existence during the voyage. There was a set food ration, physical exercises, school classes and dancing. To protect their valuable cargo from disease and avoid the expense of being quarantined on arrival, the ships did not call at any ports en route. With luck and good management it was quite a lucrative trade. A Sydney partnership, John Gilchrist and John Alexander, was agent for several Bounty ships, one of which was the *Percy*. When it sailed from Greenock on 21 May 1841, on board was the seventeen-year-old farm labourer, Patrick Mayne.

Young Mayne was tall, strong, and darkly handsome.

He had the makings of a big man, and a temper as quick as his ready wit. He was also ambitious and possessed the drive and single-mindedness to realise that ambition. There was little patience in Patrick.

To leave behind the deprivation of his childhood he advanced his age to an eligible eighteen, left his four sibling orphans to whatever care was available, and set out to find a better life for himself in Australia. His entitlement certificate suggests that as a labourer in poverty-stricken County Tyrone, he had found sufficient work and food to keep him physically strong. It declared that his state of bodily health, strength, and probable usefulness made him suitable for any work. He had no physical complaints, could read and write and had been baptised into the Catholic faith by his parish priest, William Conville.

On 28 August 1841, after one hundred days of endless heaving ocean with rarely a sea-bird to vary the scene, there was a sudden calm as they passed through towering cliffs to the sanctuary of the harbour. The late winter sun sparkling on Port Jackson, with its backdrop of sombre grey-green scrub, so different from the vivid green of home, must have stirred mixed emotions in the 282 passengers on board. Welcome as dry land and the sight of settlement were, the future was still disturbingly unknown. Conflicting tension, excitement, and gut-wrenching apprehension pressed urgently, for waiting on the wharf below were groups of sun-browned men in down-drawn hats and oddly mixed clothes, some with horses or drays, hungry for their new workforce. It was time for the emigrants to leave the shelter of their sea-bound home and be whisked away to a new, perhaps still hard, temporary bondage. Sydney in 1841 was bursting with opportunity for those who sought it, but the new arrivals, mostly contracted to work for two years, had to rein in their impatience.

By 1844, Patrick had been long free of his sponsor. He was restless, and kept hearing of more opportunity further north. At Moreton Bay, six hundred miles away, the former convict settlement had received a population boost when it began selling town allotments, and the promoters and traders who seized that opportunity were short of labour. Assigned convicts were no longer available, so they sought free men from Port Jackson. Mayne contracted to come north and work for £1 a week for John "Tinker" Campbell at the slaughterhouse and boiling-down works newly erected at Kangaroo Point. This was one of three rough settlements sprawling along the banks of the Brisbane River. The somewhat swampy South Brisbane and the higher Kangaroo Point faced North Brisbane across the water; each settlement, pushed by its investors, vied to become the trading heart of Brisbane. The investors were in a hurry to obliterate the signs and stigma of the old penal colony of Moreton Bay, and to grow rich on the wealth of wool, hides, meat and cedar brought to Brisbane on the hoof, or piled high on creaking bullock wagons that laboured over range and plain from somewhere in the blue distance.

If Sydney had been a new world after Ireland, Moreton Bay bore scant resemblance to any sort of civilisation Patrick had known. It was a frontier settlement with little resemblance to a town. Each dun-coloured hamlet, carved out of the harsh surrounding scrub, was a scattered rough-and-ready mish-mash of slab or wattle-and-daub box-like cottages and shops, some mere shacks, all widely separated by rutted, dusty tracks. They were rooted like a mouldy excrescence on the bare brown earth, a future threat to the vigour of the forest-clad hills surrounding them. At North Brisbane, two substantial buildings, the Commissariat stores and the Court House, left over from the penal years, imposed a dubious authority. Each hamlet had its well-patronised, mostly disorderly hotels, eager to attract and succour the tired and thirsty bush traveller, who, after weeks of sleeping in a swag, thankfully melted into the company of the rowdy mob in the bar.

Ships, when they came, were the lifeblood of Moreton Bay. When the river steamers docked and unloaded at the Queen's wharf at North Brisbane, the precious outgoing cargo of produce that had been brought overland to Brisbane with such difficulty had to be ferried across. The dray traffic terminated at South Brisbane. The only links between Kangaroo Point and South Brisbane and their cross-river rival on the north bank were the boatmen with their ferries. These two southbank communities should have enjoyed a trading edge over North Brisbane: they were on the direct route to the inland, the Darling Downs, and the long overland haul to Sydney — but the race for supremacy was very much in the hands of the entrepreneurial capitalists. The rivalry between the three areas provided a climate of challenge. The lucky break for the smart and the hopeful must lie close at hand.

In the mid-1840s, when Patrick Mayne arrived at Kangaroo Point, that area appeared to be gaining a commercial advantage. The high-flying investor Evan Mackenzie had built the boiling-down works and added a new wharf strong enough for the ships from the Hunter River Steam Navigation Company to berth and load cargo. For a time the wagons bypassed South Brisbane and brought trade to the Point. It seemed that Patrick had come into an area where there was life, bustle and promise.

Earning a pound a week as a slaughterman gave young Mayne some reasonable independence. Close to the boiling-down works, other settlers offered cheap lodgings for the artisans and labourers employed there or at the nearby tannery or workshops ancillary to Campbell's factory. Many of the recently arrived Irish labourers who dossed in these houses proved congenial company in the evening hours, usually dissipating their wages with the boisterous mob at Sutton's Bush Inn. Very few had wives, and there was almost no unattached female company. It was a rough workingman's world.

Contrasted with the poverty and social restrictions of his youth, this new life gave Patrick a feeling of freedom; he could relax in the homespun camaraderie at the Inn. Licensing laws were lax and often disregarded, and drinking was the leveller common to all classes. The man who tethered his horse outside, or the bullocky who left his shambling team to graze some distance away might be the squatter, his son, or a trusted employee. It was impossible to tell. They all wore sweat-stained moleskins, red or blue flannel shirts and cabbage palm hats. Sometimes when a man spoke he might be recognised as a toff, but the chance of company in some sort of civilisation and the release of prolonged loneliness led many such travellers to roister uninhibitedly with the noisiest labourers. For a poor Irish immigrant this place had a smell of opportunity; it was a place where he could mix with all-comers and unrein his fierce energy and ambition. Strong on ambition, young Patrick also had an innate efficiency and business sense.

His employer, John Campbell, was soon deep in debt to the now financially embarrassed and pressing Kangaroo Point entrepreneur, Evan Mackenzie. In addition, Campbell was experiencing production difficulties at the boiling-down works. This was temporarily solved when he sold some land he had purchased earlier and was able to set up his own new boiling-down works on the downstream side of Kangaroo Point. It had a new wharf to accommodate ships and a tidal creek to swirl away the stinking effluent. But within a year Campbell's finances again deteriorated to a point where he could not meet the wages of some twenty of his staff. Without wages, Mayne and the other employees were destitute. They had nothing to fall back on. On 7 October 1846, with their pay six weeks overdue, some of them took Campbell to court to recover their money. Patrick was owed £6.1.3d. In November he had to sue Campbell again, this time because his employer's promissory notes for £10 and £2.13.4d had been dishonoured. Campbell's insolvency was complete when his creditors forced him to sell and the new owner, Richard J. Smith from Sydney, took over on 27 February 1847.

Without pay, it had been a lean and difficult three months for the lad from County Tyrone, but he gained something from the experience. In Ireland, land was everything and here in Australia it was the same. For Campbell, land had temporarily provided a bulwark against trouble. But with insufficient land to give him long-term security, Campbell's entrepreneurial bubble had burst. It was common talk that despite Campbell's failure, the Kangaroo Point boiling-down works provided a new product and was valuable to the pastoral industry. Patrick knew that he was becoming a proficient butcher, and despite the monotonous routine, this was a trade he could follow anywhere. He did not seem to mind the fact that, except when an animal broke loose and they enjoyed the chase, the daily routine was soulless. Day after day he and his fellow butchers, William Lynch and George Platt, stunned the sheep with an axe, placed it over the blood gutter and cut off its head. The hind legs were cut off for sale at sixpence apiece, and the rest of the meat chopped into slabs and the bones broken. Other workmen jammed the pieces into large steam boilers to cook before the tallow could be drained off into wooden casks. There was little waste. The blood and remnants were fed to the waiting pigs — these, in turn, when fully grown, were dragged squealing to the assembly line for the same butchering. The three men were usually kept busy all day — but they had time to talk. They developed a companionship that extended late into most evenings, after the all-pervading smell of bloody meat had been washed away.

By his early twenties the daily manhandling of heavy beasts had increased Patrick's muscular strength. The promise of developing into a strong man, so evident in his youthful frame, was fulfilled; and he presented not only as good-looking, but as an agreeably powerful young man. Brute force was in that body and in the hard, mocking slit of his mouth. But its threat was diverted and somewhat softened by chin-length dark curling hair that framed his large, dark-eyed, mobile face.

Once the slaughterhouse had transferred to R.J. Smith's more stable ownership and wages were paid on time, life at Kangaroo Point again settled into a comfortable routine of working, drinking at the Bush Inn, and, because Patrick had the Irish gift of the gab, endless talking. At day's end there was a carefree atmosphere amongst this group; its robustness suited the energy he expended. He made special friends of Mathew Stewart and his wife Honoria, who had a small cottage near his lodgings. Stewart's goal in life was to become a publican. He occasionally made a little profit from the chickens and illegally kept pigs he raised in his tiny backyard. When the pigs strayed beyond his fence, damaging neighbours' gardens, he and Honoria brawled with their equally quick-tempered neighbours. On occasions the police were summoned and the Stewarts were fined. Most of the settlers lived their lives at flashpoint. There was a certain defiance of authority and convention and not a lot of respect for the law. Brawling and drunkenness were common problems in the colony and often involved women. And what might be an explosive release of tension for those settling an argument with their fists was also good sport for the onlookers.

With no banks, very little cash was available, so most men's wages took the form of promissory notes, which were soon lodged with the publican. He gave back another I.O.U. or some cash for necessities, and ticked up a steady flow of alcohol until the balance cut out. It was not unusual for out-of-town men to sell their produce and buy provisions, then hand the promissory note to the publican. They then existed in a blissful alcoholic daze until lack of credit balance brought sober morning and a long trek back to the crow-shattered silence of their selection. From where he lived at Kangaroo Point, such distant selections suggested no promise of wealth to Patrick. Although he had been a farm labourer, he was satisfied to gaze across the river to the dark shadows scoring the dense, scrub-covered slopes of the hills, then turn back to the cosy huddle of people, talk and argument. That distant view was alien. He liked to confront others with his always definite views. For him, opportunity lay in the town. He was quick-thinking, wanting instant results. Not for him a lonely, patient battle with capricious seasons.

Strangers with money came and went. Drunken men were often robbed. That was life in the raw settlement of early Brisbane — as it is now in any metropolis. Wise men kept silent about any wealth they were carrying. But once the drunken sawyer, Robert Cox, accused his friend William Fyfe of stealing his money, speculation spread rapidly amongst the crowded patrons of the Bush Inn. Money was something most of them would have liked to get their hands on; their lack of it was chronic. On 26 March 1848, more than one hotel patron would have taken a sudden speculative interest in Robert Cox, the stranger, from out of town.

Patrick Mayne said he was not drunk on that night. The evidence indicated that at intervals during the day he had been drinking. His later business life shows that he habitually made long-range plans and did not have too much respect for others' property. On learning that Cox had money, it would be in keeping for him to cease drinking and begin planning. He was also a man who could not bear to be thwarted and was prone to react viciously with his fists, and on later occasions with a whip. He had neither respect for the law nor fear of it; when confronted by it, he could, if he chose, maintain an arrogant detachment.

What is difficult to understand is the utter savagery of his attack on the hopelessly drunken Robert Cox. It seemed the act of a demented man. Carving up the body like a sheep was one thing; butchery was his daily work and he was doubtless desensitised to such routine actions.

But the macabre placing of the parts with no attempt to hide his crime, flaunting them in view in different locations and then propping up the head so that it would stare at those who found it, was bizarre. Even throwing the intestines down the well was no haphazard disposal. Many houses had wells and kept such foodstuffs as meat and butter in their cool, dark depths. These foodstuffs were clearly protected by a weighted, fly-proof cover topping the well. This would have had to be removed for the Bush Inn's meat and butter to receive their hideous decoration.

As news of the murder spread and local folk gathered at the scene, where was Mayne? Hiding in terror at the realisation of what he had done, or remorseless and resting after a busy night? Was he agitated, or so sick with revulsion that his mind obliterated the frightful experience from his thoughts?

Violence was part of the male culture and one could speculate on circumstances which might have triggered such brutality. If he had planned a robbery and found no money, his frustration and anger could have boiled to a pitch where he lost control. But new money did come into his hands and he must have contemplated the deed to be carrying the bone-cutting instruments.

Evidence at the inquest strongly implied that Cox and Fyfe, who had been prisoners together, had a homosexual relationship. But even if Cox had propositioned the large, muscular, twenty-three-year-old Mayne, he was obviously not capable of more than the proposition in his drunken state. And in a rough colony with its dearth of women, where homosexuality was common, it is difficult to imagine that righteous indignation would trigger such butchery.

Such speculation is idle. The cold-blooded murder and robbery of Robert Cox was committed by Patrick Mayne and proved rewarding. How else could Patrick, who drank the surplus of his weekly wage, afford to marry, and the following year purchase and stock a Queen Street house, shop, and butcher's business?

In hindsight, the evidence at the inquest clearly showed Mayne's cunning and careful planning as he deliberately implicated the innocent William Fyfe as the murderer. It took a cool head to return a day later to the cook's hotel bedroom and plant blood, most likely sheep's blood from the slaughterhouse. Incompetent police work and scant knowledge of forensic science protected him. There is no evidence that Mayne recognised murder and mutilation as an immoral act; no sign of remorse. In inflicting such violent indignity on his victim was he achieving a superiority that he craved and had never had?

Knowing of his deathbed confession, it is chilling to re-read his articulate and damningly precise testimony of his own and others' supposed whereabouts on the fatal night. Such a calculating man would not be foolish enough suddenly to produce unexplained money. He was wise enough to hold back until public memory of all the incidental witnesses at the trial faded. He was helped in this by temporarily dropping from view.

Good as the busy slaughterhouse was for the economy

of Brisbane town, the effluent from it attracted sharks upstream and cast a stinking pall over Kangaroo Point and cross-river areas such as North Brisbane. The townsfolk objected frequently and loudly. Soon after the murder, R.J. Smith was pressured to move his works elsewhere. He decided to take it several miles upstream to the north-west bank of the Bremer at its junction with the Brisbane River. The area was called Moggill and the move had several advantages. Kangaroo Point land attracted good prices for homesites, whereas land at Moggill was not only cheaper, it was closer to the source of Smith's supply from Ipswich, Long Pocket, Fassifern Valley, and Redbank where the stock route from the Darling Downs and the Brisbane River Valley converged. The surrounding scrub could provide abundant fuel for his steam boilers, and the hides and tallow could be easily barged down to the main shipping wharf at North Brisbane. In early October 1848, lock, stock, barrel and staff were moved.

The new site was opposite the parish of Goodna, well away from the sensitive noses of complaining townsfolk — and far, too far, from the workmen's leisure haunts in crowded hotels. Many of his employees were bonded; they hated the move. The quiet bush had no calming effect on their tempers. To them the isolation was little better than prison. Within weeks there was rebellion and violence amongst the workers. James Millar, bonded to his employer, downed tools and threatened his boss with an axe; Smith had to carry a pistol for protection until Millar's continued violence saw him sent to gaol in Sydney.

Three others absconded; once caught, they too went to gaol. Patrick Mayne, free of bond, kept his distance from trouble and maintained his low profile until it suited him to move.

He had found lodgings at Moggill and made a new set of friends: Darby McGrath from Waterford, Ireland and his brother John, a former convict; and Patrick Pacey, an Irish tailor and political rebel who had come on the same ship as John — the *Waverley*. They had taken advantage of a new land regulation designed to provide fresh meat for Moreton Bay, which allowed them to squat on land there. Once the convict settlement had closed, people were encouraged to take up a square mile (640 acres) of land within the settled districts for pastoral purposes only. The rent was an affordable ten shillings a year but they could not enclose the land, build on it or cultivate it.

The McGraths and the Paceys, none of whom could read or write, remained lifelong friends with Patrick Mayne, a friendship which included the Stewarts from Kangaroo Point. They witnessed each other's weddings and christenings and several times in later years Mayne stood surety for Mathew Stewart when he sought a liquor licence. They all prospered, but Darby McGrath was the smart one. He became a land speculator and in fairly short time one of Moreton Bay's wealthy men. He purchased land from Moggill to Aspley, a shop in North Brisbane, claimed brother John's widow's grazing land near the rafting ground at Moggill (there were no children to inherit), and then set himself up as a gentleman at Willowbank, in the Ipswich area.

Looking at the Crown Land sales over the next ten years it seems that he was something of a mentor for Patrick Mayne's own land deals. They often attended sales together, with Darby buying the choicest, most expensive blocks and Patrick taking up the adjoining, cheaper allotments. Patrick Pacey, the former Irish political rebel, who was ultimately declared innocent of his crime, followed the pattern of many colonial men of ambition by buying a shop in Queen Street. He also acquired some twelve hundred acres south-west of Gold Creek, in the Moggill area.

It was at Moggill that Patrick, a Catholic, met a young Irish servant girl, Mary McIntosh, a Protestant from Kilkeshan in County Clare. Her soldier father, William McIntosh, was dead. Her mother, also called Mary, was a housemaid and remained in Ireland. She had carefully placed her twenty-year-old daughter under the protection of Timothy and Mary O'Donnell, farm workers from Kilkeshan who, with their two small daughters, were migrating to Sydney in the Bounty ship *Champion*. The O'Donnells were Catholics and had in their charge four other young servant girls. They left Liverpool on 12 February 1842. Like Patrick, who had sailed five months earlier, Mary McIntosh had received enough elementary education to be able to read and write. Her certificate showed that she was a housemaid, strong and with good bodily health and had been baptised at Clonlea.

The little group of friends at Moggill knew Patrick as a

big, handsome, hardworking butcher at the boiling-down works, keen to get his foot on the next rung of the worldly ladder. He may have seemed worldly and older than his twenty-four years, and he must have been very attractive to Mary — who, to her dying day, concealed the fact that she was almost three years older than he was. In a society in desperate need of marriageable women, and where marriage conferred some status on a female, it was most unusual for a young housemaid to remain single until she was twenty-six. Whatever Mary's reasons for remaining unwed during her first six years in the colony, she was feminine enough to want to pass herself off as a younger woman. It was a short courtship; on 9 April 1849, just a year after the Cox murder, Protestant Mary and Catholic Patrick went into Brisbane to be married by Father James Hanley. In that pluralist society, noted for its gender imbalance, which fostered homosexuality, most colonial priests had a soft policy on mixed marriages. Dispensations were readily given. Mathew and Honoria Stewart stood as their witnesses at the little Catholic church, converted from a former convict barn in Elizabeth Street, not far from where Fr Hanley had his cottage at Gardens Point.

For the young couple it was back to the leafy solitude of Moggill. Very soon Mary was pregnant with their first child, Rosanna. In July, when Mathew Stewart finally achieved his goal and purchased the licence of St Patrick's Tavern at Kangaroo Point, his friend Patrick Mayne had

had enough of life and work in the country. He was ready to move back to Brisbane town.

3
Law Courts & Land Deals

ON 29 September 1849, the little-known slaughterman Patrick Mayne suddenly announced to Brisbane town that he had purchased the business of Queen Street butcher, James Newbould.

He returned to a far busier town than he had left a year earlier. The area had been given a social and numerical boost by some 420 of John Dunmore Lang's Scottish immigrants who arrived on the *Fortitude* (21 January) and the *Chaseley* (1 May), and 84 more were on their way in the *Lima* (3 November). They were mainly Scottish Calvinists, better educated, better dressed, and more soberly behaved than many of the populace. The numbers meant more customers for trade. Some opened shops, offering a wider variety of goods. New buildings that filled the gaps in the network of straggling streets gave them a more established appearance, but business rivalry between North and South Brisbane remained just as strong. There was no clear indication of where Brisbane's commercial strength would eventually reign.

Perhaps precipitantly — trade had been depressed — the sole Queen Street butcher, Newbould, had decided that two years of struggle was enough; he wanted to move. His business was not advertised for sale and there is no indication of what Mayne paid for it, but a reasonable guide lies in a similar sale at the time by Thomas Dowse, the local auctioneer. Because of pressing difficulties, Dowse sold his house and attached business premises in Queen Street for £240. This amount falls well within my calculations of the amount of money stolen from Cox when he was murdered. As a single man, Patrick had barely managed to stretch his pound a week to provide his lifestyle. With two to house and feed, there could have been no saving during the past year. Now he had money and became a man of the town. As a man of property he was on the electoral role and the jury list. His property was four shops up from the banana plantation at the corner of Queen and Edward Streets. It was a small, dark, almost windowless shop extending at the back to cramped living quarters with a semi-detached kitchen, and beyond that was a narrow backyard. Here Mary, like every good village wife, kept chickens and a vegetable patch. The Maynes' education and ability to read and write was minimal, but Patrick had maximum self-esteem as his own boss.

Within months of opening his shop he was a family man, father of Rosanna, and had money in his pocket. Their daughter had been born in Queen Street on 30 January 1850. Immediately he began living up to his new status. Now it was no cocky but unimportant slaughterman who joined his uproarious friends at the hotel, but an assertive Queen Street butcher in expansive mode who displayed his new prosperity and gained popularity by readily going surety for three Irish publicans. This was a smart business move; for many years he continued to go surety for publicans at licence renewal time. The hotels all had dining rooms that served meat, so he had an assured trade. His enthusiasm to show himself as a big fellow dropped him into an early trap, however, when he went surety for the forger James Field. Patrick's money was forfeited when Field absconded. And Mayne was not quite so enthusiastic about donating to worthy causes. He made only an average donation to support the stipend of Fr Hanley and gave ten shillings and sixpence to the Hospital Fund. Late in 1851, he was to enter that hospital for ten days, but that page in the records is missing and there is no indication of his health problem.

Less than a year after he opened his shop he was summoned to court in the first of a long series of misdemeanours that brought him into conflict with the law. Despite his undoubted desire to be an important man of business, reports in the *Moreton Bay Courier* underline the fact that throughout his short life he had little regard for the law and seemed sometimes to believe that what he wanted, he could have. There are occasional indications that a dark and stronger mind-force took control.

On this first occasion, he had sighted and taken home a pig which had been sold by another Queen Street trader, Robert Cribb, to Richard Sexton of Kangaroo Point. In a district where ownership of wandering stock was frequently disputed, owners of pigs usually made their identifying mark on one ear of the animal. When Sexton's servant and Cribb's son were searching for the pig and eventually identified it as it slumbered in Mayne's backyard, Patrick's instant reaction was brute force. Strong and fit from years of handling heavy animals, he easily gave a savage beating to the two young men and forced them from his yard. The assault was proven and he was fined £2.10.6d. Five weeks later he was back in court on a similar charge.

Although 1850 was a good year with expanding trade, Patrick Mayne could not, so early in his business venture, have had much surplus money for his new, expansive lifestyle. It is possible that having established his shop and too readily shown some largess to suit the idea of his new position, he was for a time a little short of money. One of several puzzling incidents occurred eighteen months after he bought his business.

His friend Mathew Stewart was now doing well as a publican at the only North Brisbane two-storied hotel, the Donnybrook, on the opposite side of Queen Street. At two o'clock one chilly Sunday morning, Stewart was awakened by a noise at his bedroom window. His cash-box had gone from the bedside table, the window was wide open and the thief had fled to the yard by a ladder used as a fire-escape, which he had then removed. At an outcry from Stewart, Patrick Mayne suddenly appeared and joined him in the search for the thief. They found only the dropped cash-box, still with its contents of £27. The *Moreton Bay Courier* noted that the thief doubtless expected a much larger sum which was known to be in the hotel. The reporter made much of Mayne's sudden appearance but gave no explanation for it. What remains unexplained is how Patrick appeared so conveniently on the scene at 2 a.m. Mary, six months into her second pregnancy, was in bed at the back of their shop some distance away. On that night was Mayne sleeping at the hotel in the same street as his shop, or simply passing by?

When business was slow, one of the pleasant tasks of shopkeeping was to stand at the front and chat to passers-by, at the same time noting who was in town and the amount of trade being done elsewhere. It was on such an occasion that Patrick again crossed swords with the law. In the course of duty, Constable Monsell was escorting an obstreperous drunk past the butcher's shop to the watch-house when he was suddenly and forcefully attacked by Mayne. In court, Patrick declared that he did not approve of Constable Monsell's actions.

Mary Mayne was as quick to attack as her husband. When Mrs Sheehan, the neighbouring publican's wife and her male servant attempted to retrieve their hen and chickens, which Mary had captured and carefully trussed up with string in Mayne's backyard, the all-in brawl ended in court. Screaming threats to kill, Mary rushed at Mrs Sheehan with a fence paling, while Patrick, with the bullying tactics of the larger and stronger man, grabbed the Sheehans' terrified servant by the hair. Holding him up, he enquired tauntingly: "Now what was the matter?" The "Chicken Hash" as the paper reported it, came only three weeks after Patrick's attack on Constable Monsell. Bullying, sometimes backed up by the use of his whip, seems to have been one of Mayne's ego-boosters. In the early sixties he was pilloried in the press for this standover behaviour.

In his earlier brush with the law over the misappropriation of Sexton's pig, he had considered that even though the crime was his, his home with its yard was his castle, not to be violated. But he did not extend that concept to other people. In 1855, when he asserted that another Queen Street butcher, John Wilson, had stolen eight of *his* pigs, he stormed into Wilson's shop to inspect the evidence and tried to take the pig carcases back to his shop. Both men were now prosperous butchers, with neighbouring poorly-fenced stockyards at Breakfast Creek. It was not unusual for disputes over pigs to arise. Once again, Mayne was out of luck. The carcases he claimed were minus their identifying ears. He lost the case. More than once he was accused of stealing other people's stock, but, in fairness to him, a widespread attitude to livestock seemed to be: "claim what you can get away with." Both butchers admitted that the fence was not pig-proof, and their shepherds testified that the animals sometimes became mixed. The record shows that Mayne was often careless about the confinement of his animals, and was fined several times for allowing his pigs to stray into the street.

In his many other court appearances he was fined £10 for trying to intimidate a witness; fined for using bad language; and again charged with assaulting a man in the street. This time it was Thomas Holland who was walking past his shop. A fine of £10 to a pound-a-week worker may have been a deterrent, but the moneyed Mayne displayed an air of insouciance as he paid the fine in cash, on the spot. When Martin Fletcher was on trial for forging and uttering, Mayne, who proudly informed the court that he was a butcher, landed proprietor and owner of the Lord Raglan Hotel, was accused of "acting in concert" with his hotel's publican as a witness for the prosecution. The judge decided their accusation was trumpery and threw out the case. It was another occasion when Mayne had no conscience about implicating an innocent man.

In the rough colonial culture of the 1850s, this continued flouting of law and order may have made him appear, in some eyes, something of a folk hero. For the gregarious Patrick it was important to be a big fellow; fear of losing that identity would ensure his continued larrikinism. Even the arrival of six children over that decade and the death of one of them, made no impact on what he saw as acceptable behaviour. Larrikinism has a boundary that stops short of extremes of human behaviour; in Patrick, an element of irrationality smudged that boundary. At times it seemed as though his consciousness of other people's feelings was non-existent.

After he won public office in 1859 and served with some of the town's respected businessmen on the first municipal council, his openly cavalier attitude to the law did not seem to change. Ten months after winning office, he was convicted of horsewhipping an intoxicated William Taylor who entered his shop, called him "Paddy" and gave him cheek. If Patrick thought his civic dignity was at stake, he had two assistant butchers behind the counter who could have escorted the drunk away. Instead, their employer savagely slashed at Taylor's head and shoulders six or seven times with his whip, then closed in and attacked him with its butt, inflicting more lacerations. He was fined what seemed to be the customary amount for such behaviour: forty shillings, plus ten shillings and sixpence costs.

It was always a different story when Patrick believed he was wronged. He was quick to charge indentured employees who absconded, and to see they received three months' hard labour. And he was not beyond withholding a worker's wages if it suited him. In 1846, as a slaughterman for Campbell, Patrick had twice taken his bankrupt employer to court for back wages. Yet he had no sympathy for his own employees, trying to survive with little pay. Nor did he have the excuse of trading problems or bankruptcy when he failed to pay the German migrant Heinrich Bowger for a year's work in 1858. On the contrary — he was a very wealthy man, regularly purchasing tracts of land in the town and outlying areas. Bowger, who was under bond to be employed by anyone who paid his fare to Australia, had accepted Mayne's offer of £30 a year with rations. A shepherd's wage was £40 a year with rations; the balance of Bowger's wage was to be forfeited in repayment of his fare. He won his case against Mayne, who had paid him only £14.7.6d, less than six months' wages, for twelve months' work.

In the young colony, wealth, mostly invested in property, was the indicator of social worth and success. Mayne had invested his accumulated wealth in property, and the local lads may have applied that measure of social worth to him. But those who administered the law were well aware of his lawless reputation and made no concessions. The wording of press reports of his misdemeanours occasionally suggests that the editor of the local newspaper regarded him more as one of the likely lads, a tearaway rather than a civic-minded, respected citizen to which one of Patrick's personae aspired. But it must be emphasised that if anyone other than Patrick himself harboured inside knowledge of his deepest secret, there is no evidence that the press or the general public ever suspected his involvement in the Cox murder.

In the 1850s it was not just the accumulation of land that stirred the commercial pulse of the colonists. The excitement of the Californian gold rush, and the discovery of gold by Edward Hargreaves in 1851 at Bathurst, New

South Wales, roused visions of quick riches amongst Australians. People dreamed of a bonanza. The newspapers and the people talked GOLD. In Moreton Bay it was rumoured to have been found in the Taylor Range at the edge of settlement, as well as on the Darling Downs, and hopeful prospectors panned the local creeks. Some local men had shipped off to the Californian diggings; now Brisbane's traders were concerned that not only would new immigrants prefer to go where gold had been discovered, but that Brisbane would lose many of her precious few citizens to the hunt for quick wealth. These business men, fearing financial loss (and themselves not immune to gold fever) set aside their trading rivalries and united to seek a profitable solution. On 27 June 1851, a North Brisbane group gathered in John Richardson's storehouse and pooled their money to offer a reward to a discoverer of gold in their trading area, the northern district of Stanley, or on the Darling Downs. There were enough glittering visions for the handful of men to contribute £900.15.0d., but they were cautious enough to limit the offer to the next four months. Donations ranged as high as £50, a year's salary for many workers. Patrick's substantial £20 was well up with the majority. In fact, despite the traders' qualms about a deserting workforce, not a great many people were motivated to leave the safe huddle of the settlement and brave the hazards of snakes, thirst, and unfriendly Aborigines that might await any greenhorn prospector in the bush.

The population of Brisbane had doubled in the six years since Patrick arrived; two-thirds of the 2,500 settlers were his Irish countrymen. There were new hotels serving meals to travellers and visiting squatters, and the ratio of women to men had improved so the increase in marriages meant there were now a few hundred more homes and families to be supplied with meat. Patrick Mayne's world was comfortable, the future promising. He had no money worries, his virility was obvious (Mary was pregnant again), and in his brushes with the law he could afford its fines and show he was not someone to be pushed around. In this world, money in the pocket did not confer status unless people knew you had it. Other than land there was precious little to spend money on in order to indicate success, but land was what Patrick wanted. In his twenty-six years of life in Ireland and the colony, he saw that those who owned land were the important ones. They gave the orders, lived in large houses and collected the rents. Land not only gave status, it was negotiable in times of need. It was also quite profitable when sold to incoming migrants.

Mayne's land accumulation began in August 1851, when he purchased the first allotments in what would become a holding of fifty to sixty different areas of Moreton Bay, totalling in excess of 1,700 acres. More than half his land lay in what is now the Brisbane area. This does not include his short-term trading in town shops and houses, neither does it include the Mayne family's twentieth-century gift of land to the University of Queensland for the St Lucia campus. That gift was money. No Maynes at any time owned that land.

Patrick began with two choice allotments in Queen Street; within three years he owned land in Elizabeth, Creek and Margaret Streets and at North Quay, as well as large areas of scrubland at Heussler Terrace and Milton, and thirty-five well-wooded acres facing Breakfast Creek, the area which is now Mayne Junction. In the next two confident years before the 1857 slump, he acquired land in Edward Street, and added eight acres to his paddocks at Breakfast Creek. He also bought some of the green hills of Wickham Terrace, where there began a trend for the wealthier to build; and a five-acre tract across the river adjoining the South Brisbane reserve (between Vulture, Stanley and Merton Streets). In the town he bought two hotels, the Sawyers Arms and the Lord Raglan. When the economy picked up in 1858 he began buying again, this time more land fringing the straggling streets of the settled town area, then west from its North Quay boundary towards Milton, taking in what is now the Lang Park area.

The sales of Crown land in Moreton Bay were eagerly awaited, and except in times of economic slump, the allotments were rarely passed in. Much of the land was scrub or semi-bush and it was purchased for resale for housing or rented for agricultural use. In the boom years large profits were made, but for the small speculators who could not afford to hold on during the periodic economic slumps, land investment was a risky gamble. The dealings of the big speculators were normally a passport to town eminence and Darby McGrath and Patrick Mayne were among the big buyers. Again and again the same names are listed as regular buyers, among them the town's leading businessmen, such people as Robert Cribb, Ambrose Eldridge, T.B. Stephens, George Raff, John Markwell and George Edmonstone. With the exception of the uneducated Mayne and McGrath they were men of lower middle-class backgrounds and some education; except for Markwell and McGrath, they were all to play a role in colonial and local government.

Despite their wealth, the community standing of Mayne and McGrath depended to some extent on the social solidarity of the large Irish population. Among the more staid, better educated Scottish and English townsfolk, who were less than impressed by Mayne's public behaviour and the McGrath convict connections, there was considerable social reticence. To them Mayne always remained merely a business acquaintance. He earnestly aspired to be, and became known as a man of the town, but he failed to achieve acceptance as an equal. This must have left the private Mayne struggling with a sense of alienation and frustration. Astute as his mind was for cunning action and business planning, there was a mental block which meant that he continued to behave in the same anti-social way; he expected that wealth alone was sufficient to bring him social success.

In 1859, Patrick Mayne was one of the considerably land-rich men who successfully stood for the first municipal elections. In that year the Collector of Customs, W.A. Duncan, moved to Sydney and Mayne purchased "Dara", his cottage at the edge of semi-bushland on Duncan's Hill (Centenary Place). A typical first settler's house, it was primitive but liveable, with a flat roof and wattle-and-daub walls propped up by hardwood joists fixed against the outer walls. Its real value rested in the fact that its hillside commanded a vista along both Queen and Adelaide Streets. It was one of Patrick's rental properties, and in 1861 the Catholic Bishop, James Quinn, became his tenant. Two years later, as part of his continual buying and selling at a good profit, Mayne sold it to the Church. In these years as an alderman he bought another eighteen acres in the Lang Park area, several allotments at Sandgate, a large section of Kelvin Grove and two town allotments at Lytton. Following James Toohey's lead, he also bought 140 acres at Yeerongpilly. Some of the money to fund these land purchases came from the rents paid on his recent investments in buildings. He acquired the Brisbane, British Empire and Royal Exchange hotels, all rented to publicans. Rents also came from his Cafe Nationale and shops and houses in Queen, Edward, Leichhardt, Albert, and Adelaide Streets, as well as houses in William and Creek Streets, slaughter yards at Enoggera, and the paddocks at Elizabeth Street, Moggill, and Breakfast Creek. A few of these properties were mortgaged, but as Brisbane's population doubled from 6,051 in 1861 to 12,551 in 1864, he shared the general confidence that both his trade and his future rents were secure. There was also a widespread belief that before long gold would be found to take care of the future.

There was no doubt about Mayne's business ability. In addition to his busy shop, he wholesaled meat to J. Gibson, the butcher at South Brisbane. And for some years he had been developing a strong trade in hides, tallow, and sheepskins. Once regular coastal shipping became available, he advertised that he would ship goods on reasonable terms. As his business expanded and flourished, he needed to buy and fatten his own stock. This required rural land, not too far out, but close to the route for his supply in the grazing districts. In a deal with T.L. Murray-Prior he began paying off 693 good grazing acres at Moggill. It was now only a short step further up the ladder to the world of graziers. He would breed his own stock on his own broad acres. In September 1862, fourteen years after he had robbed and murdered Robert Cox, Patrick Mayne arrived at the top of his colonial ladder. He took a five-year lease on the 32,000 acre Rosevale Station, but borrowed heavily to buy outright the pre-emptive homestead area of 640 acres and stock the property.

This was good cattle land, watered by the upper Bremer River on the eastern side of the Great Divide. Life was indeed satisfying. His business acquaintances may not have been his best friends but his rise to fortune was openly spoken of as one of the colony's success stories.

4

Consolidating an Empire

THERE was a great deal more to Patrick Mayne than barbaric behaviour and the accumulation of property. He had an innate ability to plan meticulously for long-term action and not deviate from his decision. Despite all the cunning and savagery of the Cox murder, it clearly reveals this ability. Once Patrick crossed the poverty line and stepped into a more satisfying world where he was a man of business, his still untutored mind channelled its instinctive ability to make wise choices for long-term business success. Where others made hope a paradigm for their future, Patrick made use of vitality, action and single-mindedness. His negative, darker, satanic self, which unwisely exploded with savage aggression to minor irritations was not subdued, but he seemed able to separate it from his world of business, where he remained mentally in control. He had decisive ideas to increase his own wealth and his community standing and to benefit the town. Despite burdening himself with a large number of civic and private projects, he retained for some years the determination and concentration to steer them to successful conclusions.

In the first four years as shop owner and man of property, he consolidated rapidly. Young Rosanna, and Isaac (born on 14 January 1852), both named for Patrick's parents, played in and out of the shop and the backyard. Mary was pregnant again, and although the Maynes were considered a bit too rough to be on the visiting lists of most of the other Queen Street traders, Patrick had established himself as a man who could move with the times and afford to keep up with the best. By 1853 the worst of the prevailing depression was over. There was a rising real estate market, and changes in Queen Street reflected confidence in the future of the area. Robert Cribb began building his new brick drapery establishment, Moreton House, with its Sydney-style fashionable plate-glass windows. Patrick followed suit, but planned differently. He began with a new large brick home across the road from his shop, near the Edward Street corner of Queen Street. Both Cribb's and Mayne's modern premises were much admired, but Patrick was only beginning. He added an adjoining brick shop. In November 1853, just after their second daughter, Evelina Selina was born the complete move was made and he proudly advertised his butchery's new location. A block away at his recently purchased yard at the corner of Elizabeth and Albert Streets, he could slaughter his stock at sundown, hang it overnight and quarter it early; even in the hottest summer he could now provide freshly killed meat for his customers.

It was to be expected that his new shop would include a meat room built with charcoal between the walls to keep the meat cool, but with the convenience of his Elizabeth Street yard, he could quite profitably slaughter only every two or three days. At the end of the first day any unsold meat would be rolled in dry salt and drained. But there was no real problem with waste meat turning black or becoming fly-blown. European housewives were accustomed to "hung" meat which they trimmed if necessary, washing it with wine or vinegar before cooking.

Patrick Mayne also established himself as a man to be counted on when the town rallied for a cause. His name appears on a wide variety of lists. Together with those who bought land in the North Quay area in 1853, he petitioned the Government Resident, Captain Wickham, for the rough tracks called George and William Streets to be made passable for horses and carriages. The following year he added his name to the petition for a bridge to link North Quay with South Brisbane. When Queen Street rallied behind the "reverend republican", John Dunmore Lang, with a request that he represent the Stanley Borough in the Legislative Council of New South Wales, Patrick's name was published on the supporters' list. With Tom Petrie, Hobbs the surgeon and twenty-two other leading townsfolk, he petitioned the Governor General to exercise clemency and remit the last year of the sentence of Patrick Irwin, a ticket-of-leave holder. (Their request was turned down.) His signature in those days was awkwardly formed, as though by a hand unused to writing. Occasionally he tried a flourish of loops and swirls but they show no fluidity, and a certain lack of penmanship.

In 1853, a second reward for the discovery of gold was offered, and Patrick's increased contribution of £75 joined those of the eighty-five hopeful townsfolk who put up £2,825. These leading townsfolk rallied for a variety of reasons. On one occasion they raised over £500 as a reward for information about the malicious stabbing of a horse. In that horse-oriented society such a sum is an indication of just how necessary a good riding horse was, and how difficult to replace. Beyond the town boundary the lack of decent roads and the density of the scrub, with its rocky ridges and shallow rifts, could prevent a horse and cart or even a bullock and dray from travelling very far. Butchers needed to ride out to find straying stock; others rode to their new allotments; and — important to most of the entrepreneurs — a horse was vital for inspection of the uncleared outlying Crown land which the government intermittently released for sale. Even where there were discernible roads it was not uncommon, after rain, to find a lumpy bullock wagon bogged to its axles, barring the passage of all other wheeled vehicles. A sick or damaged horse could hobble a business man for a long time; this was why, to stop that sort of vindictiveness, John

McCabe offered £100 reward for information. Almost every other trader, Mayne included, put up £5 each: in all, £513.11.0d. was offered. This was the equivalent of ten years' wages for a labourer or butcher's assistant. The reward was not claimed; the culprit was not caught.

From the beginning Patrick Mayne's name is always well down on the variety of published lists, and throughout his life it continues that way. In a list of fifty or more names, his will be somewhere in the last half-dozen. These lists were rarely alphabetical; they clearly show a hierarchy of townsfolk. Always at the top are names such as Petrie, Cribb, Elphinstone, Raff, Markwell, Stephens and Eldridge. It begins to look as though Mayne is frequently among the last to be asked — or, alternatively, he does not offer, but has to be asked. The latter is unlikely. Reading his character from what is available, he actively sought a civic role and he also knew what was good for business. Most probably, as town scallywag who did not fit the others' idea of respectability, he was one of the last called on and the last listed.

There are some lists on which his name does not appear. They usually involve donations which would provide little benefit to himself. In the Patriotic Fund list of 1855 for the war in the Crimea, the establishment and bourgeoisie names are there, led by pastoralist William Tooth, who gave £100. They also include, well down on the column, "Mr Chinaman Leon" and "a poor man" who each gave 2/6d. It is not surprising that Mayne is absent; in keeping with the political scene in Ireland, there is a conspicuous absence of Irish names. In the same year, a well-received fund to help the town shows an average donation of £3. Again, "a Chinaman" gave £3, but Patrick, clearly out of step with the other Queen Street traders, reluctantly gave £1.

One sad period in these years must have been the death of the baby Evelina Selina, who lived barely a year. Born in October 1853, she died, like so many of the colony's infants, in the warm, fly-blown months and was buried in November 1854 in the new cemetery at Paddington. There is no indication whether the death of Evelina was a time of great grief, or whether it was stoically accepted in a colony where more than half the children failed to live beyond the age of five. Patrick's energetic organisation of his growing empire left little time for his family. At the time of Evelina's death, his brand-new acquisition of fifty-nine acres at Breakfast Creek urgently required fencing and stocking before the cattle belonging to his neighbour, Elphinstone, started grazing on his summer grass. There was no break in Patrick's frenetic extension of his business or his activity in town affairs.

At those new, extensive cattleyards at Breakfast Creek, and his holding paddock in Elizabeth Street, he employed shepherds. There were up to two butchers in his shop and at home he hired a servant girl for Mary, who was soon pregnant again this time with William McIntosh whom she named after her father. Most certainly there would be someone to mind lively Rosanna and young Isaac. As well Patrick employed two fencers to split timber and fence the

Breakfast Creek yards, then his land at Milton and elsewhere. He had a minimum of nine people on his payroll and continued to expand. His idea of work was not simply to extract every physical ounce of labour out of his men. He was efficient, and his orderly mind made him want to fix what he saw as intolerable government inefficiency. In September 1855 he called his own public meeting to discuss an amendment to the law relating to slaughtering of sheep and other animals within the colony of New South Wales. There is no record to say whether he attracted any supporters, or, if he did, the result of the meeting.

As more immigrants arrived, the pressure on rental housing became acute. It was another opportunity for gain for those with money. In 1855, when the usual town worthies called a meeting at the Exchange Rooms to re-establish a lapsed building society, Patrick offered himself as one of fifteen committee members. As usual, at the head of the list were the businessmen Buckley, Cribb, and Markwell; Mayne was number fifteen. They issued 151 shares of £50 each and were confident that by the next meeting they would reach their target of 200 shares.

Patrick Mayne's energy must have been prodigious. He had confidence in his ability to organise and manage affairs and by the mid-1850s he was seeking involvement in almost every event in town. His ability was recognised by many others: he seems to have been accepted and actively involved in many financial and civic spheres of town life. Between his jousting in the court for his law infringements and his prosecution of others, his work at his yards and shop, his hides and tallow trade and his property investments, there were political and town business meetings to attend and petitions to sign. His civic involvement was vocal as well as physical: he was never one to remain mute in a gathering. The minutes of the early Council meetings reveal the scope of his advice and suggestions on town matters. He enjoyed vigorous debate, and at times his aggression makes him appear a thorn in the side of others present.

In August 1855 he was a signatory calling for John Richardson to come forward as a candidate to represent the Borough of Stanley in the by-election caused by the resignation of Henry Stuart Russell, MLA. Six months later, his name was listed with John Markwell, George Edmonstone, and Robert Cribb as members of a committee favourable towards the return of Henry Buckley for the County of Stanley. The following week he was appointed to a committee to promote the re-election of John Richardson. All these endeavours were successful.

Meanwhile, the idea of colonial separation was in the air. The people of Moreton Bay had many grievances against the Government so far away in Sydney. At all the political meetings the candidate enthused his audience when he spoke rousingly about Government neglect of basic needs such as a bridge to link north and south Brisbane, the untrafficable roads and the abysmal lack of a decent water supply. By the New Year of 1856, the people had reached a ceiling of frustration. The enthusiastic and vocal Mayne was at the lively separation meeting on 23

January 1856, but his signature on the petition tail-ends that of thirty-two of the town's leading citizens.

Neither his public nor his business life were ever dull routine. Even bonded employees put their heads up now and again and caused him trouble. The system of bonded employees was well established and generally worked well for both parties. It had secured Patrick his passage to Australia and a chance to establish himself. But sometimes the system failed. He had bad luck with several Germans. One of them, Jacob Schelling, died in mysterious circumstances. After Patrick's death in 1865, this tragedy was one of several apocryphal stories that was to haunt his children.

Schelling was a herdsman at Mayne's bullock paddock, next to George Parsons' farm at Milton. For almost two years Schelling's accommodation had consisted of a large box about 150 yards from the waterhole in the paddock, which was some six feet deep. It was part of the watershed that fed Western Creek. The waterhole was his laundry tub, his bath, his water supply — and his death bed. He was a melancholy man who suffered fits of depression, a good target for a bully. It does not take much imagination to accept that on his pitiable days Schelling would have been a source of irritation to Patrick, provoking intimidation and constant harassment from his belligerent employer. Appearing to be frank and open, Mayne told the inquest into Schelling's death that his employee was "terrified of him". Ten months earlier, an attempt by Schelling to hang himself from a tree had been aborted when the neighbouring farmer, George Parsons cut him down. On that occasion Mayne had remonstrated with his employee, giving him a tongue-lashing. Such castigation would have done nothing to ease Schelling's suicidal depression. He was clearly a nuisance to Mayne, but still under bond. Two weeks before his death, when Mayne was killing a bullock (and quite likely accompanying it with a verbal attack on Schelling), the terrified man had begged his boss not to hang him. On 9 February 1858, one of Mayne's labourers was sent on an errand to the German but could only find his shoes by the waterhole. He hurried back to Queen Street, where Mayne suggested that Schelling had drowned himself. The two then returned to Milton, and with George Parsons' aid Schelling's fully-clothed body was dragged from the waterhole, and with it a spare pair of trousers. Patrick suggested he may have been washing them.

At the inquest next day, Dr Barton gave evidence that the body did not present the appearance of death by drowning. There was more rigidity of the limbs than he would have expected, and the forearms were flexed on the arms. There was an unusual congestion about the face, with a good deal of frothy blood about the mouth and eyes, as well as dark marks on his posterior. Since Schelling had a brother of unsound mind in the Brisbane Hospital and there was no evidence to show how he had died, the case was closed without further investigation.

Perhaps the need to manhandle Jacob Schelling's body from that watery grave triggered disturbing thoughts in the dark recesses of Patrick's mind. The inquest over, he walked up to the solicitors Little and Rawlings to make his will. He was thirty-three, wealthy, with a young wife and three very bright and lively children. His will provided a very generous £100 each to the brother and three sisters he had farewelled in Ireland, and demonstrated his enduring care for his wife, Mary. She was to inherit £300 a year in half-yearly instalments, and if she remarried she would still receive £100 a year, which in those days, would have provided adequately for her needs. He gave total power to the executors and trustees of his estate. They were the influential merchant and entrepreneur, George Raff, and Patrick's cousin, Joseph Darragh, whom he had sponsored in 1850, and trained and employed in his butcher shop.

Darragh's wife Eliza had spent those years as Mary's servant. Like Patrick, Joseph Darragh had been a farm-hand at Cookstown, but after three years' training with Patrick, he opened his own butchery at Kangaroo Point and was soon on the road to wealth. He was a singularly cruel and uncaring man. After twenty-three years of ill-treating his wife, the mother of his eleven children, he violently threw her into the street and began to cohabit with a young local girl, Mary Merritt. Although he owned property valued at £20,000 he abandoned Eliza with no means of support.

In 1858 Patrick could not have foreseen the final outcome of the Darragh marriage, but as both Joseph and

Eliza had worked and lived on his premises, he must have known something of his cousin's constant ill-treatment of her. Women at that time were frequently held in contempt; knowing Patrick's own explosive temper and penchant for cruelty, one can only speculate about how he treated his own wife and children.

Raff and Darragh were appointed guardians of both the person and the inheritances of Patrick's children — his boys until they turned twenty-one, his daughters during their "minority and discoverture". This clause, which embraced spinsters, divorced wives or adult widows, was common where large fortunes were concerned; it is particularly interesting in the light of Patrick's death-bed confession, and the directive that none of his children was to marry.

Whatever Patrick's role in Schelling's death or any disturbing thoughts he may have had after it, they were quickly put behind him as his business activities claimed his time and continued to fill his coffers. Rents came in from two hotels, the Sawyers Arms and the Lord Raglan, from shops, houses, and farmland, and from the auctioneer R. Davidson, who hired his stockyard in Elizabeth Street for periodic stock auctions.

For Patrick Mayne, the zest in life came from being on the scene, in the thick of things. A number of the more affluent colonists had built substantial English-style stone, brick or timber houses set in small farms or large gardens;

it was not the beauty of nature that gave him joy but action, talk and money-making. At no time did he try to change his home from the hemmed-in Queen Street shop site to one of the less central but more fashionable town boundary areas. In fact, in 1858 he advertised for rent a cottage in four acres of good garden adjoining the town boundary and the Brisbane River. It was one of an unknown number of properties he bought and sold in those years. In the same advertisement he sought a tenant for a dwelling in Edward Street.

That year Mary had been pregnant since April. Cooler, dust-free river air away from the stinking open drains and privies of the town buildings would have been more comfortable for her during the sweltering summer before their daughter, Mary Emelia, was born on the last day of December, 1858. Another pleasant area would have been the site of "Dara", which Patrick snapped up a few months later. It had a most desirable location but the simple house, with its mud walls did not seem to Patrick to match his affluence and self-esteem. When the Church subsequently bought "Dara", the parishioners were no more enamoured of it as a desirable home than Patrick. They considered it too crude a building for their Archbishop. In 1890, with Dunne as Archbishop, they raised £8,000 to build an elegant, three-storied Italianate mansion, the second "Dara". Unfortunately, this architectural gem was not to remain a part of Brisbane's colonial heritage. A later Archbishop, James Duhig, blew it up to make way for the foundations of his special project, the never-to-be-built

Holy Name Cathedral. For decades the site was a sleazy haunt for the homeless. Now, as Centenary Place, it is an up-market area of high-use home units. Of this fillip to town trade Patrick would have heartily approved.

1859 was a landmark year for the northern portion of the mother colony of New South Wales. It was an even more lively and satisfying year for politically ambitious colonials in the area. The separation movements, initially led by the squatters and taken up by J.D. Lang, a member of the Legislative Assembly of New South Wales, eventually succeeded with the hesitant Colonial Office in London. On 10 December 1859 the Colony of Queensland, with almost 30,000 inhabitants, was established. Patrick Mayne had added his name to lists at separation meetings, but of more immediate importance to him was the agitation for Brisbane to be incorporated as a municipality.

For nine years, ever since he had become Brisbane's new butcher at the age of twenty-five, and made his presence felt, he had been increasingly active in civic matters. He was now thirty-four, still belligerent, still handsome, and wealthy and successful. By remaining at the heart of things in Queen Street he knew everyone and they knew him. His large presence and colourful lifestyle made him ever-popular with the socially cohesive Irish community and he was known in the town as a man who worked for town improvement. If Brisbane was to become a municipality, he wanted to bring his vitality to a role on the council.

Patrick shared this political interest with George Raff, ten years older, a highly respected and a socially prominent merchant who planned to stand for the first Queensland Parliament. Other than wealth, business, and a desire to work the levers of power, the two men appeared to have very little in common. However, the fact that Mayne made Raff an executor of his will and was associated with him in a few business ventures suggests that for some time he had seen the older man as a mentor whose standing in the community enhanced his own. At this time there was clearly a political alignment between the two. Raff counted on Mayne and his Irish following for political support, and on his cooperative financial support for politically important causes such as the National School Fund.

In June 1859, a fund was opened to subsidise the under-funded secular Brisbane National School, and Patrick, along with many others, donated £2. W.A. Duncan, the Customs Officer, who represented the Catholic interest as a patron of the school, was leaving and another Catholic was needed as his replacement. George Raff, already a patron, and astutely aware of the uneducated Mayne's political aspirations, was probably instrumental in ensuring a second donation, this time of £100 from Patrick. Mayne was publicly hailed as a generous donor, made one of the patrons, and, as such, was invited to replace the Catholic Duncan on the temporary Board of Education. He then took practical action to demonstrate his belief in the school. Nine-year-old Rosanna remained with her teacher, but his first-born son, Isaac, aged seven, was enrolled at the Government's Normal School, a forerunner to that near Adelaide and Edward Streets. In that act Patrick was now seen as a supporter of the needs of all the town's children, not just those of the Irish Catholic immigrants.

Perhaps it was on Raff's advice that he curbed his larrikinism and avoided trouble with the law. From June 1858 until August 1860, well after both local and Queensland Government elections had been finalised, he managed to stay out of court. But the brutish characteristics in his nature were always there; he could not suddenly become docile. The press record suggests that he still threatened people with his whip, but for that period, he apparently did not use it.

By the time the heated debates on incorporation had resolved themselves and the municipality of Brisbane was proclaimed (7 August 1859), thirty-seven candidates were ready to contest the nine aldermanic seats. Five weeks later the town's businessmen were runaway winners: John Petrie (builder and contractor), Patrick Mayne (butcher), T.B. Stephens (tanner and fellmonger), Joshua Jeays (architect and builder), A.J. Hockings (seedsman), George Edmonstone (butcher), Robert Cribb (baker and land agent), and two innkeepers, George Warren and William Sutton. Of the 1,519 votes cast, John Petrie, educated, able, and possibly the most respected man in the settlement, topped the poll with 325 votes. Patrick Mayne, with little respect for the law, but a wealthy patron of the school with a glib Irish tongue and boundless enthusiasm and energy, achieved

274. At last his name was high on a public list, proudly second instead of being at the tag-end, and ahead of the educated, socially accepted and wealthy T.B. Stephens, who had become part-proprietor of the *Moreton Bay Courier.*

It had not been easy to find nine good men who wanted this unpaid responsibility. On election, Petrie contented himself with promising to discharge his duties faithfully. Mayne declared that he would concentrate on work rather than talk, and was sure that his election reflected the appreciation of the community for the work he had already done. Stephens implied that he had not solicited election, but would accept office as a matter of duty. "Honest Bob", Robert Cribb, known for his simple tastes, austere habits and personal kindness, was further down the poll. Petrie and Cribb were men for whom Patrick and the townsfolk had great respect. Petrie appears to have kept a business length away from Mayne, but Cribb, more charitable towards his fellow men, offered the Maynes neighbourly concern at several times of need.

All nine aldermen were practical men. Most had some formal education, a few had almost none, but they had all made their own successful way in a rough, uncaring colony. Seven of them were bearded and soberly dressed and looked the epitome of city fathers; the clean-shaven, nattily dressed Sutton and Mayne both had police records. Sutton's was related to being drunk in charge of his hotel. One wonders what dark and fearsome thoughts whispered in Mayne's mind at meeting after meeting as he sat opposite William Sutton in Council. In 1848, those two men, with Lynch and Platt, had been post-midnight drinking companions at Sutton's Bush Inn a short while before Patrick Mayne murdered Robert Cox, and Sutton had been arrested as a suspect.

Patrick's role as school patron had been worn with great success during the municipal elections. In the Council's first meetings he showed himself to be a practical, cooperative alderman. It says something for George Raff's political power in the community that in February the following year, the *Queensland Government Gazette* listed Patrick Mayne as one of the Governor's nine appointees to the first Board of National Education in Queensland, serving under the presidency of Sir Charles Nicholson. For the ambitious Mayne this was a real distinction in the community. He was not only sitting as an equal at the same table as educated members of the establishment, but helping to make decisions for the education of their children. He could be excused for thinking his social alienation was over: around the table were the highly respected Hon. Robert Ramsay Mackenzie, Daniel Rountree Somerset, George Raff, William Thornton, Charles Tiffin, Henry Jordan and Henry Day.

Patrick's success as an alderman, and now his pride in what he saw as an exalted role, became too visible and too audible. Some townsfolk were not willing to accept an upstart, almost illiterate butcher on their Board of Education. They had no difficulty in accepting a successful butcher as an alderman, but this appointment was an affront. Shock and anger turned to ridicule of the man. Rumours spread like a bushfire and the blaze was quickly out of control. It was said that "Patrick Mayne was too big for his boots; now he planned to stand for Parliament." There was no objection to other aldermen who later successfully stood for the State legislature, but Mayne they did not want. The rumours grew. The smirks and derision were undisguised. Patrick was disparaged from all sides. The effect on a man of his explosive temperament must have been devastating. In three weeks the "hate" campaign against him reached a point where the Executive Council had to step in to protect its decision, publishing a rebuttal of the scuttlebutt in the *Moreton Bay Courier* of 8 March 1860. It read:

> "Some of our contemporaries have been amusing themselves by poking fun at Mr Patrick Mayne and the Executive Council on his appointment to the seat at the Education Board of Queensland and we are now in a position to state the circumstances of the appointment. When Dr Milford and Mr Duncan left it became necessary to find some person to represent the Catholic body at the National School and Mr Patrick Mayne was considered most eligible by the other patrons; and when it was thought desirable to place a master in the school, the executive appointed those who had been patrons as a temporary board. When Mr Mayne became patron he contributed the munificent sum of £100 for the purpose of forwarding the objects of the school. It will be very fortunate if as good grounds can be shown for public appointments generally as for this one; but we do not admire the taste of

> those who, because Mr Mayne acquired wealth by honest industry, should seize the opportunity afforded by his anxiety to forward education, to reproach him with his misfortune that he is not an educated man. If his co-religionists and co-patrons deem him fit, what right has anyone in this community which embraces principally wealth with ignorance and ignorance without wealth, to point to Mr Mayne? He is a city alderman elected with a large majority and has fully justified the choice of his fellow citizens and we believe him to possess much more common sense than most of his detractors. If any more were required to show the petty animosity displayed on this occasion, it would be the fabrication of the report that Mr Mayne is a candidate for the Legislature — it is devoid of truth."

Harassment of Mayne did not vanish overnight. Open season on him lingered for several weeks but, after the Executive Council statement he immediately took his own action to regain some lost prestige. In the *Moreton Bay Courier* of 20 March he called for public tenders for the erection of a stable and coach-house. The shortage of trafficable roads made the acquisition of a coach something of a trumpet flourish, but he, Mary, and the children would ride in as much style as any educated town doctor or high government official. Two weeks later he called tenders for the erection of two more imposing brick shops in Queen Street.

The parliamentary election campaign was gearing up. Mayne's close political association with George Raff had fuelled the false rumours that he, like Raff, would stand for parliament. He made an obvious show of being out and about and involved at all the rallies. He proposed the shipping agent, Henry Buckley, to represent East Moreton, seconded John Petrie's nomination of Raff, and constantly and loudly down-cried D.F. Roberts, a solicitor and member of the Queensland Club, who aspired to represent Fortitude Valley. In retaliation, Roberts, who called himself "the Poor Man's Friend", refuelled the anti-Mayne campaign with an advertisement in the *Moreton Bay Courier* of 1 May 1860:

> **ELECTORS OF FORTITUDE VALLEY**
>
> **Be early at Poll and vote for Daniel Foley Roberts the Poor Man's Friend.**
>
> **That great man with a smart whip in his hand by name Mister Paddy (I mean) Mr Patrick Mayne, says that by a wave of his magic whip he can undo all that the friends of D.F. Roberts have already done.**
>
> **ELECTORS OF THE VALLEY HAMLETS**
>
> **Don't be gulled by what you may hear from Mister Alderman Patrick Mayne Esq. He thinks he can ride over you like he can a bullock.**
>
> **HURRAH FOR D.F. ROBERTS**

From this it is clear that Mayne had faced down some of the early ridicule in his customary manner, confronting his detractors in his rage and bitterness with the threat of his stockwhip. He also continued to display the power of his wealth by spending another £100 on two town lots at Lytton and eighteen acres of prime land at Enoggera.

Then, abruptly, he went to Sydney. He left behind a newly pregnant Mary — she was carrying their last child, James O'Neil — and was absent from the new Council for the next five consecutive meetings, but there is no explanation of his absence. Had he been on Council business the minutes would have recorded it. In Moreton Bay this was a time of business optimism. Land prices were high and he was rich in land. He had sensibly slowed his buying during this last twelve months of a seller's market. He was a player in the building boom and his two latest modern shops were well on the road to completion.

One might question why a man so actively interested in politics should choose to be away at a time of great celebration to culminate their political efforts — the opening of the first Queensland Parliament on 29 May. It was also quite out of character for him to leave town when his political opponents were biting at his heels, and not to oversee the construction of his expensive buildings. Two things could have taken him on that uncomfortable lengthy trip to Sydney. A need to seek private medical attention during the anti-Mayne period of mental stress; or the need to raise a large loan from a Sydney bank for further business expansion. No other immediate business expansion took place, but by September 1860 he had accumulated a sizeable debt with the Bank of New South Wales.

Soon after his return, his Queen Street shops were opened (July), to be hailed in the *Moreton Bay Courier* as an imposing feature of Queen Street's architecture. One shop was let to Mr Kosvitz, a jeweller and watchmaker, and Mayne was congratulated on the plate-glass windows and brilliant gas lighting which enhanced the display of wares. His use of acetylene lamps, the first in Brisbane shops, was an innovation exciting to a populace accustomed to the limited illumination of oil lamps. It predated the general use of gas lighting by several years. But this show of wealth, business acumen and self-confidence was not enough. Public ridicule of him had reflected on the Executive Council. Six months after the announcement of his nomination to the temporary Board of Education, the *Government Gazette* published a new list: the name of Patrick Mayne was missing.

5
In and Out of Council

THE municipality of Brisbane under the first Council's charge consisted of several settlements. North Brisbane was centred on Queen Street, which, with its houses, shops, and banana plantation, was a convenient thoroughfare to the eastern settlements of Fortitude Valley, Nundah and Sandgate. The area of North Brisbane also included Adelaide, George, and Elizabeth Streets and adjoining areas with residences dotted here and there. A ferry ride across the river were North Brisbane's two rivals, South Brisbane and Kangaroo Point; but the Point, with eighty or ninety houses and some industry, was no longer a real threat to Queen Street. That hope had been picked up by Fortitude Valley, which was strengthened by J.D. Lang's migrant scheme, and saw itself making a strong challenge.

The mainstream religions had claimed their hallowed patches a stone's throw from some of the central hotels and a brewery. Four banks eased the earlier difficulty of circulating cash for trading, and the new hospital in George Street and the new gaol on Petrie Terrace catered to the needs of the area's 5,000 people. Thanks to astute and civic-minded men such as Cribb and Mayne, a few substantial business premises stood out, but for the most part the public buildings were mean and unimpressive. Everything was deplorably neglected. Sanitation conditions were primitive; there were open sewers, and their effluent, dumped near houses on the river bank, was a menace to health. Depending on the weather, the rough streets could be dusty and rutted or else deep bogs interspersed with uncrossable muddy pools. In the rainy season, adroit shopkeepers were known to keep trade coming their way by spanning a street pool with a plank. It was not uncommon to hear cries for help from a pedestrian bogged in the mud. In Adelaide, Elizabeth, and Charlotte Streets, in reality only rough passages between allotments, whole areas could be isolated by deep, unbridged water-filled culverts. The so-called "reservoir" was an unfenced, dammed-up waterhole lying between George and Roma Streets. In drought it dried up and water had to be carted from Breakfast Creek. People bathed and swam in it and washed their clothes there and dogs and cattle drank from it. Its creek, often a chain of waterholes, meandered across the site of the present City Hall and the intersection of Adelaide and Albert Streets, then swept in a wide curve through what are now the two Queen Street blocks separated by Edward Street. It turned north to cross Creek Street at its corner with Adelaide Street, then made a wide down-curve through the next block, crossing what is now Eagle Lane, returning in a series of loops to Creek Street at its junction with Elizabeth Street. After a large, boggy circular loop at the rear of the site of St Stephen's Cathedral, it entered the Brisbane River near the junction of Mary, Creek, and Charlotte Streets. For some it was still known as Wheat Creek and much of the surrounding area continued to be used for agriculture.

The task ahead of the first councillors was enormous. Lacking a Council building, their first meeting was held in the Queen Street police barracks, with the Police Magistrate supplying their furniture, before they were given a temporary office at the Court House. Their first year's budget was expected to be £1,000 — that alone was needed for the reservoir and drainage. The municipality was in urgent need of the energy and practical commonsense of its nine aldermen.

In politics, as in life generally, Mayne was always determined to have his say on everything. He was quick to nominate people and projects, and to second other people's ideas. He immediately and successfully nominated John Petrie as Mayor. When he moved that a committee be appointed, he always named himself and those other aldermen he thought should work with him. These suggestions were neither wild nor Machiavellian. They reflected his enthusiasm and practical approach. All the aldermen were men of property. In nominating a committee to revalue the assessable property in the municipality, his sensible suggestion was of men of the most experience: Petrie the builder and contractor, Jeays the architect and builder, and Cribb and himself, whose extensive and successful land purchases showed they had a businesslike understanding of the varying value of allotments. Patrick was a man who got things done, and he embraced civic problems with a wrestler's grip. Bullying tactics and cunning were intricately woven with his shrewd business sense. Business ethics played little part in his life. He argued that instead of sending out rate notices, a list of names and rate assessments should be published in the newspaper. For those who failed to pay by the due date, his solution was to publish their names in the social pages. He thought that disrespectful letters should be returned to the sender, and when a Mr Porter lodged a complaint about a surveying matter followed by a notice of action, Patrick moved that they put it into the wastepaper basket. The over-worked Town Clerk fared no better. In 1861, he requested a rise from £200 to £250 a year; Mayne abruptly moved that if the Clerk was dissatisfied, the Council should put the job out to tender.

He had trouble differentiating between what could be expected of aldermen and paid Council employees. The aldermen, unpaid, spent hours away from their own business affairs as they inspected and discussed the young town's enormous problems. It had not been easy to find suitable townsfolk who thought the personal cost worthwhile, but for the young, energetic and wealthy Mayne the opportunity to administer the affairs of the town and the status it gave him more than offset the responsibility and the sacrifice in time and finance. As a butcher he could recoup nothing, but some of the other aldermen were in a more fortunate position as contractors or suppliers of stone, timber, or imported items for the roadworks and buildings. While he never failed to grasp an opportunity to make more and more money for himself, he was not too keen on council contractors making much profit. He kept a practical, businesslike eye on Council finances, especially tendering, always looking out for signs of jobbery. He always called for the lowest tender to be accepted and closely watched the job to ensure it was well done and on time. This did not endear him to those aldermen who secured Council contracts.

There is no doubt that in his first term, Mayne, at thirty-six, the youngest alderman, was an authoritarian but very useful and energetic member. He worked hard on several committees to improve the town environment. He was a tidy man, neatly dressed; he liked a good appearance in everything. The buildings he had put up enhanced the townscape. His *bête noire* was vandalism which defaced and damaged town buildings. He clearly could not catch the culprits — otherwise he would have personally whipped them off the street. Instead, he urged the Council to post a £5 reward for their apprehension. Although he was one of the wealthiest men in town, his lack of social acceptance by the bourgeoisie kept him a man for the workers. Much of his contribution at that time reflects that. He succeeded in moving that "all children, not just those at denominational schools, travel free on the ferries", but he had less success in trying to gain the same concession for cross-river church-goers.

Understandably the pressure of their own business caused most aldermen occasionally to miss meetings. In the Council's first term Patrick had been away from mid-May to late June; eighteen months later, he was again absent from mid-December 1861 to mid-January 1862, another five weeks. Alderman Cribb reported to the Council that he was away on urgent private affairs. This was immediately followed by the necessity of his standing down as one of three annual retirees, and a subsequent lacklustre performance in the February 1862 municipal election, when he failed to re-take his former seat. Alderman R.S. Warry replaced him. The title of alderman had given him a status that made up for lack of social acceptance. The role of alderman gave him the power he wanted to organise and run things and argue how he thought they should be done. In view of his desire and need for this role, his long absence just prior to an election is surprising. His lacklustre performance may have been due to the fact that serious illness was beginning to manifest itself, or that some lingering aspects of the anti-Mayne campaign of ridicule still worked against him. In a burst of political energy he registered his family as parishioners at the little Catholic church in Duncan Street, Fortitude Valley. It was from here he hoped to gain more votes at the next election.

From 1863, when he again stood for Council, this time successfully as representative for Fortitude Valley, his irrational comments and behaviour gradually became more obvious. If he felt Council proceedings were becoming tedious, he would produce his "monocle", a leather ring the size of an eye-glass. According to John Cameron's reminiscence, if an alderman deviated from the facts or exaggerated, Mayne, who was rough in manner, would deliberately and ostentatiously place the leather ring firmly at his eye and stare at the speaker in a comic manner, to disconcert him and cause general laughter from all the others. This glass-less leather ring had such an unnerving effect on some aldermen that on one occasion the question was asked as to whether it was not a breach of the law to use a leather ring in the form of an eye-glass.

In August 1863 Patrick began a four months' agitation over the fire bell. With others he had approved its cost of £30, but when he found the installed bell had cost £50, he belligerently moved that it be dismantled and returned and a new one procured, not exceeding the sum voted.

Brisbane was no stranger to fire. There was no reticulated water supply, no fire brigade, and the clusters of combustible wooden buildings with their oil lamps, naked candles and wood stoves nightly housed far too many incautious inebriates. Their safety and survival could depend on the clanging of the fire bell for quick action to limit a fire's spread by a bucket brigade and others with piles of soaking blankets. Mayne was well aware of the danger. Ever since he had built his brick home and shops, which were flanked by flimsy, combustible timber buildings, he had advocated an end to timber construction in the business area. Such vulnerability was devastatingly proved on 11 April 1864, when a large tract of Queen Street West was lost to the flames. One side of the block was almost annihilated when one hotel, fourteen shops, two houses and numerous offices were incinerated. Even the brick buildings were vulnerable because of their highly inflammable shingle roofs. There were no water carts, and all the private tanks in Queen, Albert, and Adelaide Streets were emptied to meet the demands of the fire, which was halted only when men of the Twelfth Regiment chopped down the North Brisbane Hotel and two shops to make a fire break. In the subsequent unprotected condition of the town, nineteen men and women were charged with stealing from the piles of salvaged goods which the frantic shopowners had stacked for safety in the street. The people had always known that they were impotent to save valuable buildings from fire; they lived with that constant dread and insecurity. Only a few days before that fire, a meeting of protesting townsfolk had called on both Government and Council to finance some means of fire protection for their homes and businesses. The Council factions, too busy struggling against each other, did nothing. With that common knowledge, Mayne's months of intransigence over the fire bell was in contradiction to his call for fire control and new building regulations. His haggling over the cost of the fire bell strained the patience of other councillors.

He was becoming more argumentative than usual, and in division was almost always against the motion unless it was his. In Council, it sometimes seemed as though his motions were no longer the product of his practical mind but drawn from the grumbles of the groups of labourers with whom he drank after work. He certainly got a short shrift from the very hardworking business aldermen when he proposed that in the summer months Council labourers should be granted a three-hour midday siesta from 11.30 a.m. to 2.30 p.m.

Argument over the water supply rumbled on for years, but during the 1863–64 debates on water resources, parliamentarian George Raff's manipulative influence on Mayne might be suspected. Intimating that he had privileged information, Mayne moved that the Government and not the Council was the proper party to be trusted with the supply of water to the town. At this time politics were being played fast and hard between the Council factions as well as between the Council and the Queensland Government. His rambling, accusatory attacks on fellow aldermen inflamed an already testy issue. He argued that the Council was not capable of carrying out the work properly, that the Government had no faith in the Corporation of Brisbane and planned to take over the work. He then attacked the civil hydraulic engineer, Mr Oldham, arguing that the Government could obtain the assistance of scientific men and would not employ men who had broken down in other parts of the world. Neither would the Government encourage worthless flunkies who were able to do nothing. Therefore he thought the waterworks should be entrusted to Government management. When he was accused of borrowing ideas, he pledged his word that his motion "came out of my own head which, though a big one, has plenty in it." Obstinate to the end of the debate, he stood alone when the rest of the aldermen were determined to resist the Government.

He missed seven meetings during 1864 and the Council minutes suggest that his contribution to debate had little of the commonsense and vigour of his first term. In February 1865, when it was customary to elect the Mayor for the year, the factions within the Council began jockeying to have their man elected. The competition descended to squabbles; Mayne, determined to be heard, seemed to be in some state of confusion. He nominated John Petrie, then seconded the nomination favouring Alderman Pettigrew. The arguments ranged over two discordant meetings before Alderman Hockings was elected Mayor.

To some extent Patrick's usual rough tongue and bellicose stance and the faction-ridden breakdown of reasonable debate must have masked his changing health and irrationality. He was again elected to the Finance Committee. This lasted just over two months before it became clear to everyone that he was a very ill man. Because of his continued absence, Alderman Graham officially replaced him on the committee. Towards the end of May, a nurse was engaged for him, but he struggled to his last Council meeting on 5 June 1865. From then on until his death on 17 August, he needed full-time nursing at his Queen Street home.

6
Life in Queen Street 1860–1865

DURING Patrick's busy aldermanic years his business life had surged ahead. The anti-Mayne campaign of early 1860 had dinted his ego but not his self-confidence. His last child, James O'Neil Mayne, was born on 21 January 1861. In that year he commissioned the architect Benjamin J. Backhouse to design two more brick shops; when finished they were let to the drapers Grimes and Petty and the grocer, Reuben Oliver. Politics and persecution were temporarily off the town's agenda, and he saw a heaven-sent chance to strengthen his social standing in town.

In Brisbane's isolated community, visitors were always a

source of interest. In 1861 a young gentleman from England, the guest of Colonel O'Connell, was much talked about for his charm and skill as a pianist. He was seventeen-year-old W.R.O. Hill, the son of a military officer who claimed acquaintance with Lord Palmerston. When the Colonel introduced Hill to various people in town, Mayne invited the lad to stay at his house for a few days. In his memoirs, Hill, who became a Police Magistrate and Gold Warden in North Queensland, recalled that he went in, sat down at the piano and rattled off a few lively airs to the entire satisfaction of the family. Mayne immediately made him a very generous offer of £1.15.0 a week, plus board and lodgings and a horse to ride, if he would give piano lessons to eleven-year-old Rosanna. Unfortunately for Patrick, that chance to close the wide social and cultural gap was lost. Hill declined the offer; he wrote that although he was a musical athlete, he played by ear and did not know a single note of music.

The economy of the early sixties was buoyant. Raff, Stephens, and a coterie of moneyed townsmen formed the Queensland Steam Navigation Company with a capital of £60,000. Mayne was one of the shareholders. Raff, who had once been a partner in Lamb, Parbury and Company in Sydney, had a background in merchant shipping and they planned a regular steam service between Brisbane and Sydney, upstream to Ipswich and, in the future, to North Queensland. Mayne's interest in this new company greatly widened his business horizons. Shipping meat was one of his plans, but more opportunities kept presenting themselves.

At this time, Australia was being promoted in Ireland as a land of small farms where prosperity and political independence were available to all. Under the Immigration Regulations of 1861, new settlers who paid their own fare or those who sponsored them were reimbursed with an £18 land order. The Q.S.N. Company quickly became involved in sponsorship on a company basis and some of the major shareholders also operated individually. Under his personal sponsorship, Patrick first paid for four migrants, one of them his mother-in-law, Mary Kelly, who had remarried and was again widowed. He then paid for nine other adult migrants from Ireland, one of whom was his sister Ann. He earned land orders valued at £234 which he was granted after their arrival in 1862.

At the same time, Bishop Quinn set up the Queensland Immigration Society, which was to alleviate continued stress and poverty in Ireland and swell the numbers of his Catholic parishioners in Queensland. The Society was administered in Ireland by Father Robert Dunne, who processed the migrants and farewelled the first ship in February 1862. From then on, it was to be followed by one ship a month. In the first year three thousand Irish Catholics were sponsored by Quinn's society, but by the time the exodus to Queensland reached six thousand, Bishop Quinn foolishly remarked that the colony should be called "Quinnsland".

Sectarian hostility was common. It grew with this big

intake of Irish Catholic migrants, and Quinn's immodest claim was the spark that caused an explosion. That, coupled with the fact that the scheme was proving too costly and the high death rate during the long voyage was causing loss of income, saw Quinn's immigration society dissolved in 1864. The scheme's importance to the life of the Mayne family lies in the fact that Fr Robert Dunne, who had processed and farewelled so many of his countrymen, arrived in Moreton Bay as Quinn's Vicar General on 10 December 1863. He was to influence most of the future life of the Mayne family, and indirectly the gifts to the University of Queensland.

Although Patrick failed in the 1862 municipal election, he must have viewed his business life with pleasure and satisfaction. Wherever he rode around Brisbane he could feel a surge of pride as his glance embraced the extensive property he owned. Confidence and commercial optimism were everywhere. Land prices were high and he had plenty of it to supply the building boom. In addition, several Government and municipal projects were absorbing labour and encouraging business. His own business plans were long-range and thorough.

The Q.S.N. Company ships plying upstream to Ipswich sought regular profitable cargoes. He and other station owners walked their stock to Ipswich, but for efficiency and maximum profits, they needed a regular fat cattle and sheep market in that town. For the buyers this had to be supplemented by reliable, regular river transport to Brisbane, which would be provided by the Q.S.N.

Company. Mayne and other Brisbane butchers, including Edmonstone, Darragh and Baynes, made a public appeal to Fattorini and Company of Ipswich to establish that regular market. This move gave some security to his plans for his new property "Rosevale". And the fact that he currently had no council business to eat up busy hours gave him the time to devote to this, his biggest project.

Mayne always had to be a front runner. Once he had set up "Rosevale" and the shipping project, he wanted to be back where he could have a wider say in the town's affairs. His scattered landholdings made him eligible to vote and stand in more than one ward, which was how he stood successfully for Fortitude Valley. In the jockeying to elect the Mayor, he shifted his allegiance from John Petrie to the man who had backed him in his call for the Ipswich fat stock market, George Edmonstone, another butcher. They were involved with others in business ventures and Edmonstone was a man of property, some education, and stood well in the town's hierarchy. His nomination of Edmonstone was successful. Perhaps, if one butcher could be Mayor in 1863, another butcher, the ambitious Patrick Mayne, might be so elevated a few years hence. For now, he had to be content with being nominated to the Incorporation Committee and the Lighting Committee.

Lack of water was a serious problem for everyone, but too much water was a far more serious threat. In March 1863 constant rains flooded much of Brisbane town. The river and Wheat Creek overflowed, surging through lower Queen Street so that all the premises on the west side between Edward and Albert Streets were flooded. The Maynes, in their solid brick shop and home with its stables and coachhouse, suffered along with their neighbours. This must have caused anxiety, loss of stock and trading, and costly repairs — a new stress on a man who, as the Council minutes show, was beginning to display increasing irrationality in his actions.

With a man as belligerent and unstable as Patrick, who had no compunction about the pain he might inflict on others, it seems reasonable to accept that his behaviour within the family could be similarly unpleasant. Rosanna, now fifteen, was being taught by the Sisters of Mercy at the new All Hallows' School in "Adderton", Dr Fullerton's former home across the way from Bishop Quinn's "Dara". Isaac, thirteen, and William, nine, were at the Normal School at the corner of Adelaide and Edward Streets. All three were old enough to have been affected by their father's behaviour, especially his rages when he was thwarted. It is highly likely that the tragic adult life of Mayne's children, while partly hereditary, may also be attributed to his treatment of them. It is fairly significant that Mary Emelia, six at the time of her father's death, and James, a toddler of four, were the least affected of his children.

Mary Mayne, their mother, proved to be a particularly strong woman. Unschooled she may have been but she was capable and intelligent, and, if she could not do much to protect the children who were old enough to defy their father and incur his wrath, she would have ensured some protection of the infants. There is no evidence that her mother, Mary Kelly, lived with the family or was any help to them. She died, and presumably lived, at Bowen Hills, but appeared to have no money; she may have occupied one of Patrick's houses. Ann Mayne, Patrick's younger sister, who had lived with them for barely a year, was probably reluctant or unable to stand up to the brother on whom she was entirely dependent. The man who gradually took a benevolent interest in the family was the new Vicar General, Fr Dunne. Mary Mayne remained a Protestant, but seemed to find more acceptance among the Irish Catholics than with those of her own religion. The children were brought up in their father's faith. Patrick's wealth, his lack of whole-hearted commitment to the Church, and his inclination to stray from its teaching meant there were plenty of reasons for Fr Dunne to call on them. His coming into their increasingly stressed life must have brought some comfort and strength to Mary.

Fr Dunne was very different from the other Irish colonial priests they had known. He was a stocky man with a round face given character by a sharp nose and gentle hazel eyes. After an education in Rome, followed by some years as a teacher at St Lawrence's School, Dublin, he had the strength and confidence to be tolerant and compassionate, and was also worldly-wise. He tried to solve his parishioners' very human problems by employing a common sense that allowed him to interpret Church law to suit colonial circumstance. From fragments of letters that remain it seems clear he was aware of problems in the

Mayne family, and extended what pastoral care he could. His worldly advice may well have been behind the sudden switch of fourteen-year-old Rosanna from day-student to boarder at All Hallows' in 1864. The school was only four blocks away from their Queen Street home.

For a man who was mentally and physically ill, 1864 was far too heavy a year for Patrick. If the cause of his death was porphyria, syphilis or cancer, by this time he was probably affected by it. Having been elected to the Council's Finance Committee he was involved in preliminaries for the new Town Hall project and the cross-river bridge. There were interminable arguments over the urgently needed water supply, and the people were demanding a new hospital. True, the population had risen to 12,551 which meant increased rate money, but it was never enough to catch up with the town's most elementary needs.

In his business sphere he was shipping meat, supplying other butchers, and trade at his shop was brisk. There was his hides and tallow trade, and rents came in regularly from his many houses, business premises, paddocks and farmland. His directorship of No. 3 Building Society provided a fair income, and the Q.S.N. Company was doing well enough for him to substantially increase his shareholding. He was known as an astute businessman with very substantial assets. The Bank of New South Wales had readily lent him money for further expansion, especially to stock "Rosevale" and purchase the pre-emptive square-mile homestead block. T.L. Murray-Prior gave him credit to buy his large grazing tract at Moggill. His personal interests were now so widely scattered, so diverse and demanding that they may have been the reason that throughout the year he missed at least one Council meeting a month.

If one adds to his private workload the additional Council work, there may lie the answer as to why he now failed to keep a strict eye on all his financial affairs. That had not been his regime up until now. Perhaps business was so good that he missed the signs of downturn and believed a little wild financial gambling was nothing to worry about. But it is more likely, in such an astute man who had watched others fail by overreaching themselves, that by 1864 he was losing the concentration and tight grip that had directed the accumulation of his wealth.

The pre-dawn tragedy that had hit the business heart of Brisbane months earlier, when a large tract of Queen Street West was incinerated, had not involved loss or damage to any Mayne property. However, the cost had been enormous to town trade, insurance companies, and owners of other premises, some of which were not insured. To cap it all, the cracks in the economy were beginning to show. Prices rose and credit was tightened. Unable to afford to rebuild, some licked their wounds and quietly went bankrupt, leaving their creditors to go into deeper debt. Others patched and painted and began trading again. For a while the scope of the financial damage was not clearly realised.

In October, Patrick's and other councillors' agitation to improve the appearance and fire safety of Brisbane was taken up by newspaper proprietor and alderman T.B. Stephens. Mayne seconded the successful motion that the upper part of the town between Ann, Alice and Saul Streets be proclaimed "first-class". All new town buildings were to have external walls of brick.

Seven weeks later, on Thursday, 1 December 1864, Brisbane's worst-ever fire began in Stewart and Hemmant's corner drapery and blazed out of control uphill until it had consumed twenty-two business premises, the new Music Hall, and some forty houses in the block bounded by Queen, Albert, Elizabeth, and George Streets. Lost in the blaze were four drapery stores, three hotels, three restaurants, two banks, two butcher shops, two saddleries, and others supplying groceries, fruit, confectionery, oysters and jewellery, as well as the auctioneer's mart. Most of the destroyed wooden houses had been crowded behind the Queen Street shops and occupied by the poor. The fire was only prevented from sweeping along George Street when a group detached from the hundreds of voluntary fire-fighters was able to demolish Mr Pillow's humpy to make a fire-break. The *Brisbane Courier* reported that 6,000 people gathered to watch the great fire. This time looters were held at bay by redcoats from the Twelfth Regiment with fixed bayonets, parading in front of the smouldering ruins as the conflagration ate its way through the rest of the unprotected block. At its height the flames and sparks roared so high that for some time the survival of the opposite side of Queen Street was in doubt, even though the buildings had been smothered in wet blankets.

Mayne was not among the butchers who were burnt out, but his new brick shops, praised for their brilliant gas lighting, were in ruins. His tenant, Kosvitz the jeweller, had time to save only some of his stock. The Mayne account entries for repairs to burnt premises reveal that the Cafe Nationale and at least two of his houses also suffered. The *Brisbane Courier*, which gave much space to naming the leading townsfolk who were especially prominent in their exertions to save property, listed all the usual hierarchy of names, all aldermen or town businessmen, but made no mention of Patrick Mayne.

Was this because of the continued non-acceptance of this very wealthy alderman as a social equal to those other townsfolk? He was too large a man to remain unnoticed, too aggressive and authoritarian to have done nothing. His own properties were at hazard and it is inconceivable that he and his staff were not helping. The *Brisbane Courier*'s constant overlooking of Mayne when he could have had positive publicity must raise the possibility that there may have been an undercurrent of dark and shadowy suspicion about his link with the long-ago Cox murder, or even that of the German herdsman, Jacob Schelling. There may also have been an element of this in the anti-Mayne publicity when he was nominated to the Education Board in 1860. Dismembering and drowning feature in the many stories that still surround the family name.

The fire cast a gloom over the whole community. Through Christmas and into the new year people were faced with a variety of shortages, including festive fare. Neither could they escape its daily reminder in the stark, charred black stubble of stumps and walls that spiked the wasted street. Not only the streets were ruined. Ruined businessmen either could not or were slow to pay their accounts and mortgages. Some had lost everything. There was no money to spare. Somewhere in all of this there was a tilt in the fine balance of the solvency of the speculating Patrick Mayne. For his last two large property purchases he had seriously over-borrowed. It took only two costly, unforeseen town fires and their aftermath to agitate the town bankers waiting beyond the widening economic chasm. He was now unable to meet their pressing requests to reduce his considerable debt. Some time earlier, he had sub-leased all but the homestead area of "Rosevale", relieving himself of the £80 a year Government rental. The land at Moggill was also rented to a farmer, but now there were no rents coming in from his burned town premises and no ready money to repair them.

Most of the townsfolk regarded the big, colourful character Patrick Mayne as one of the colony's success stories. He was still a relatively young man and had risen rapidly from rags to riches. Perhaps his deteriorating health had made him careless of the fact that other traders and customers owed him almost £4,000. Whatever his health problem may have been, the new year of 1865 saw him a sick man, heavily in debt to T.L. Murray-Prior and an impatient Bank of New South Wales, at a time of downturn in the economy. He was also struggling to maintain his role as an alderman in a quarrelsome, faction-ridden municipal Council. If he recognised the pressure, the stress must have worked against him.

There were plenty of assets which could have been sold as a simple solution to his pressing debt. But it was not a good time to sell, and he was not about to have a fire-sale of his valuable properties. He believed that those who retained their assets won the game. His temporary shortage of money had to be traded away. Quite evidently his usual quick, clear mind was not grasping the seriousness of his own or the general economic position. At this stage he was having difficulty in coping with both his life and his business. Unfortunately, the page is missing from a record of his ten days' hospitalisation in 1850, and the slot for "cause of death" is blank on his death certificate. The secret of his health problem remains.

On 25 May 1865, Patrick went with the other aldermen to the Governor's levee, but aldermen were not important enough to be presented to the Governor. He managed to attend the next Council meeting, which must have demanded real determination. Within days, his illness was such that he needed a full-time nurse in attendance. But that meeting dealt with the imminent opening of the first timber bridge to span the river at North Quay. He had long battled for its construction, and his role on the Finance Committee had given him some meetings of satisfying arguments. He was not destined to take part at the opening.

If life for Patrick had become either a drift into a world of shadows and phantasms or a misery-ridden bed of pain, it must have been something of a nightmare for Mary. No one could doubt that her irrational and ill husband would be difficult to nurse. Moreover, on 4 March, her mother, who had arrived only two and a half years earlier, had died aged sixty-four. Patrick contracted to finance her funeral and burial in the Milton cemetery, but the account remained unpaid. Rosanna and Isaac, now two high-spirited and wilful teenagers, who both proved later to be damaged children, were not easy to control. In her travail Mary turned to the understanding and caring Fr Dunne.

7

Crisis After Crisis

AS the cold winds of July 1865 chilled the winter days, all those close to Patrick knew that he had little time to live. On top of Mary's concern and grief she was faced with the bank's pressing demands, the huge debt, five young children and a multiplicity of scattered business ventures about which she knew nothing, as well as the butcher shop, which she valiantly kept trading. It was clear that they would depend on this for their immediate livelihood. The two executors, George Raff and Joseph Darragh, were no doubt helpful with advice, but Raff was preoccupied with Parliament, his many involved business ventures, and the imminent foundering of the Queensland Steam Navigation Company, which had been waging an unproductive price-cutting war with the southern-based Australian Steam Navigation Company. Joe Darragh, less pressed by business, was at Kangaroo Point, on the other side of the unbridged river, not readily accessible. Fr Dunne, a good mathematician, had straightened out the Church accounts for Bishop Quinn, but he was no capitalist entrepreneur. His pastoral priorities were the care of the sick and dying and the education of the young. He had already helped Mary by drafting a letter for her requesting further education for young Isaac, who would soon finish at the Normal School.

Dunne had liberal views on education, and in Queensland he worked hard to see that bright young Irish lads had an opportunity to further their education. In 1865 he established a Catholic Young Men's Society with a heavy emphasis on education. Here he hoped to make up for the lads' lack of access to a Grammar school. Some he prepared for the Civil Service examination. Young Andrew Thynne he prepared for law. The Maynes, too, would come under his watchful eye and influence.

Dunne had long been disturbed by the apathy and defeatist attitude common to far too many young Irish migrants. They seemed content to remain on the bottom rung of colonial society. In Patrick and Mary Mayne he responded to the positiveness and energy that shone through their rough and sometimes disordered behaviour. In the face of Patrick's imminent early death, it was characteristic of Dunne to want to ensure that the tragedy did not result in the wasted potential of their capable, bright children. He had a good ally in Mary.

At some point in the first week of August, while Patrick was still lucid, a decision was made to include Mary as a trustee and executor of his estate. The codicil, giving her equal power and authority with Raff and Darragh, was unusual for the times. Wives had little standing in the community; any status they had was derived from that of their husbands. Business affairs were considered to be far beyond their ability. The decision to include Mary suggests that she had already demonstrated that she was a capable and responsible woman. The codicil seems to have been drawn up in great haste. It was not dated, and six weeks later its legality was questioned in the court. Patrick's signature, which on his will drawn up in February 1858 was large and clear, written in a firm sure hand, was now shaky and unsure, difficult to recognise as his. But there was no difficulty in proving its legality. When the matter came to court on 22 September 1865, Robert Cribb, whose honesty was regarded as beyond doubt, tendered a letter confirming that he had witnessed the drawing up and signing of the codicil on 7 August, ten days before Patrick died. A second confirming letter was tendered by the solicitors' clerk, Walter Barber. The calling in of Cribb, a Queen Street businessman who was not a friend, to witness such a document, suggests something of the haste with which the change was made. It also indicates that several people as well as Dr Hugh Bell, Fr Dunne, the nurse, family, and maid visited the sick room during those last two weeks. The solicitor and Raff and Darragh were there, and other friends may also have made a last farewell. Any one of those could have overheard a rambling or delirious Patrick and subsequently disclose his death-bed confession to murder, which became public property some days before he died.

Anyone who had ever been harangued by hellfire preachers about the plight of the unrepentant sinner brought to divine justice and the horrific eternal hell of the damned might have shared Patrick's terrible fear. He had a few despairing weeks to ponder on his future damnation; weeks when he was suspended agonisingly between the successful man he had built himself up to be and the murderer about to face his God. Now, shrunk in illness, with nothing left, not even his size to intimidate his terror, he desperately wanted salvation.

The story was out. Patrick Mayne had committed a murder and the wrong man had been hanged for it. The town knew of it several days before he died on 17 August. The community belief was powerful and the shame and misery within the family must have shafted into their grief. The strength of Mary Mayne stands out like a beacon. The backlash in the minds of the children can only be imagined. In her boarding school, Rosanna would have nursed her pain alone, without the consoling comfort of family mealtime discussion, anger and questions to release the pent-up stress. The two eldest boys would have faced taunts and whispers, and stony eyes that followed them as they walked to school.

Mayne's confession to the murder in 1848 of Robert Cox created a surging buzz of excitement and anticipation. The public perceived that Patrick was a murderer, but most of the townsfolk had arrived after 1850; they had never heard of Robert Cox and William Fyfe. It was the old hands such as Henry Stuart Russell, Thomas Dowse, J.J. Knight, William Sutton and the Petries who remembered the case. Years later, without mentioning Mayne's name, Russell and Knight wrote of the confession in their memoirs; and Dowse, who had been on the grand jury which condemned Fyfe, made a pointed non-mention in one of his "Old Tom" articles in the *Queenslander*. Naming the traders in Queen Street, he wrote of Mayne's shop: "... occupied by another, who for prudence sake, I decline to name." To this day, the connection between Mayne and the murdered Robert Cox has disappeared. Among historians, the Cox case is occasionally mentioned as having an unsatisfactory finding. Mayne's name was omitted from the press reports at the time. He was not suggested as a suspect. Instead, the name of Mayne, without specifying which member of the family, is constantly linked with a series of disconnected, bizarre but fictional murders.

This came about because generally the townsfolk let their imaginations embroider the confession, and handed down to their children and grandchildren their own exciting versions of what happened. No one spoke out publicly about the confession. The papers could not carry it. The story remained intriguing gossip. In an isolated colonial town where the only events that disturbed the general boredom were accidents, crime and hangings (which could be counted on to draw a big crowd of whites and

Aborigines), Patrick Mayne's funeral, held on a Sunday, became an EVENT.

Head high, Mary spared no expense. The undertaker's account for £97.11.0 was well over twice the cost of her mother's funeral, which, only months earlier, had been a fitting farewell reflecting the wealth of the Maynes. Her husband had been a public figure; many civic dignitaries would attend. They did; but she underestimated the power and rapid spread of flying rumour. On the morning of the funeral the buzz of the throng in Queen Street must have seemed daunting to Mary and her sister-in-law, Ann. The *Brisbane Courier* (21 August 1865) estimated that 4,000 men and women were crammed outside the Mayne house waiting for the hearse to move off. Along the route, groups of one to three hundred people waited at vantage points for a better view.

As Irishwomen, Mary and Ann knew that they were watching for confirmation of the flying rumours. There was a strong belief in Irish folklore that when a murderer dies, the horses of his hearse will refuse to move it. Stories still abound that the horses of Mayne's hearse would not move until they were thoroughly whipped. The poet, Gwen Harwood heard the story and wrote of it in 1943. In another version, the horses baulked at the entrance to the Roman Catholic cemetery at Milton and refused to go in until they were forced. Whether or not the spectators' macabre curiosity was satisfied, they would have been rewarded with the longest funeral procession that Brisbane had seen. There were many private coaches to carry all the aldermen and the large number of leading businessmen, and every vehicle plying for hire in the town was pressed into service. Behind them came some hundred horsemen and a large number of people on foot. The *Brisbane Courier* reported the length of the procession as extending from the hospital in George Street to the gaol at Petrie Terrace. Whatever his knowledge of events and whatever his thoughts, the compassionate Fr Robert Dunne kept his own counsel as he buried forty-one-year-old Patrick beside his baby daughter, Evelina Selina who had died eleven years earlier.

The continuing care and friendship offered by Fr Dunne was unaffected by the fact that Patrick left the Church not one penny. The extent of his previous largess had been limited to a £50 donation some time earlier for Bishop Quinn's Cathedral Fund. It would have been in keeping with Church practice for the visiting priest to try to ensure some benefit from Patrick; at that time he believed him to be a very wealthy man. An appropriate time would have been when the codicil was added ten days before Patrick died, but Dunne took no advantage of his ill and frightened parishioner.

Had anyone questioned Patrick's mental state during his tempestuous life, the revelations about the Cox murder would have offered some confirmation that he had a problem. Early this century, Dr James Mayne told Dr Lilian Cooper that there were three generations of madness in his family. This must have included one of his grandparents. If Patrick had kept this knowledge from

Mary, at the time of his confession his sister Ann or his cousin, Joseph Darragh, may have revealed it. Darragh's mother Ann and Patrick's mother Rose had been the O'Neil sisters at Cookstown, Ireland.

The far-reaching result of Patrick's confession and the discussions about his mental instability was some sort of family decision that none of the children should marry. Patrick's will of 1858 had been drawn up in the belief that his children would marry and he allowed for the possibility of grandchildren. Dame Rumour still has it that the priest who heard the confession forced a non-marrying rule on the family before he consented to Patrick's burial in hallowed ground. Dame Rumour did not look at the facts. Fr Dunne had no such legal authority, and if he had made such a proviso, there was no way of long-term enforcement. In later years, in his scattered bush parish on the Darling Downs (1868–81), the compassionate priest was known to have pardoned penitents for all the sins of their past life, even the most serious transgressions, where the granting of absolution is usually the preserve of a bishop or pope. There is no reason to believe that in this case he imposed conditions on the children of the penitent Patrick before granting him absolution. There is more reason to believe that such a worldly-wise priest would know enough about his parishioners to recognise some mental instability and allow commonsense to prevail over ecclesiastical law.

There is also reason to believe that this very humane man, whose record shows that he worked hard to solve the

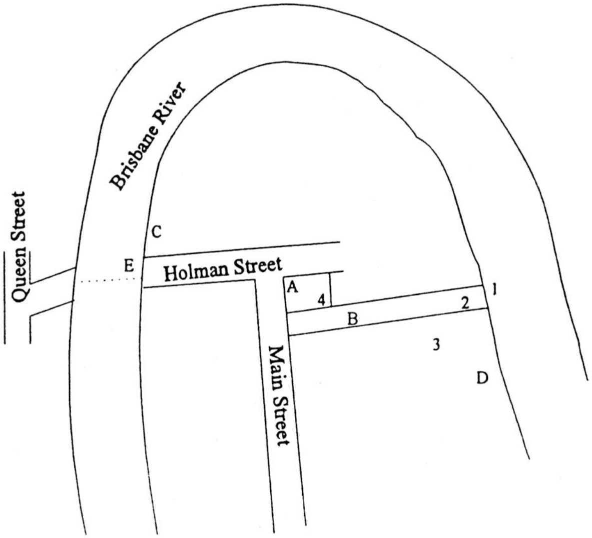

The site of the profitable murder. (Gayle L'Estrange)

KANGAROO POINT 1848

A Bush Inn
B Rankins Garden (site of murder)
C Mackenzies Boiling Down Works
D Campbell's Boiling Down Works
E North Brisbane Ferry and Mackenzies Wharf

1 Legs Found
2 Torso Found
3 Head Found at Campbell's unfinished building
4 Intestines Found in Hotel well

Note: The murder area was between the site of the present Yungaba Migrant Centre and the Bush Inn on Holman Street.

The Cox murder area viewed from Bowen Terrace. (John Oxley Library)

Patrick Mayne and William Sutton both elected to the first Council 1859. Both were at the Bush Inn on the night of the murder. Sutton was arrested. (Fryer Library, *Jubilee History of Queensland* ed. E.J. Barton)

Queen Street 1854. The butchery with home upstairs (arrowed). Here the last three Mayne children were born. (Fryer Library, Hume Collection)

Sparsely settled Roma and George Streets were wide open for land speculators. (Fryer Library, Browning Collection)

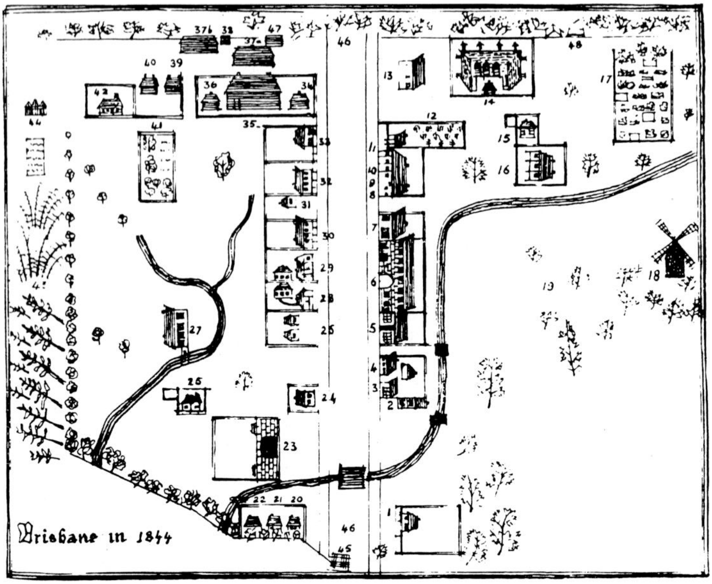

Brisbane hamlet c.1844, when the labourer Patrick Mayne arrived from Sydney. (Fryer Library, map C.F. Gerler)

Brisbane in 1844. A pictorial plan by C.F. Gerler drawn at Carlsberg, his Brisbane property, in March 1886. Gerler arrived from Germany in 1844 to assist the missionaries at Nundah. His plan is not to scale, being more in the nature of a medieval pictorial representation. A photograph of the original plans is in E.J.T. Barton, *Jubilee History of Queensland,* 1910, and the version reproduced here was redrawn for G. Greenwood and J. Laverty, *Brisbane 1859–1959,* 1959. The items keyed to numbers in the plan are as follows:

1. Andrew Petrie
2. Handel, cattle drover
3. Savory (the only baker)
4. Bensteads, sawyers
5. T. Richartson (the only general store) From the bricks of this old house the first Wesleyan Church was built.
6. Convict Barracks (afterwards Court House)
7. W. Kent (druggist shop)
8. Fitzpatrick (the First Chief Constable)
9. The Lock-up
10. The Constables' Place (only two in all)
11. Slates' Post Office (old)
12. Slates' Pineapple Garden
13. Church of England
14. The Hospital
15. Mort. milkman
16. Wright's Hotel
17. The General Cemetery
18. Tread and Windmill
19. Edmonston's sheep for slaughter
20. Old R. Jones
21. Dr. Simpson (the first Commissioner)
22. Old Major Prior
23. The Gaol
24. Skyring's Beehives (soft goods shop)
25. Hayes, milman
26. Brothers Fraser (first houses)
27. The Catholic Church
28. McLean's Blacksmith's Shop
29. Edmonston's (the only butcher)
30. Bow's Hotel
31. Taylor Shappart
32. Montifeur (a financier)
33. W. Pickering (now Bank of N.S.W.)
34. Sergeant Jones
35. Soldiers' Barracks
36. Officer De Winton
37. Commission Stores
38. Queen's Wharf (the only one)
39. Captain Wickham's Office
40. Commissioner T. Kent
41. The Commissioner's Garden
42. Captain Coley
43. Government Gardens
44. Father Hanley (the only Priest)
45. Saw Pits (late Gas Works)
46. Queen Street
47. The Boat House and Boatman's House
48. The First Tombstone (two graves)

The heart of Brisbane Town 1862. Rapid expansion provided an awesome challenge for the first Council with its budget of £1,000. (Fryer Library, Browning Collection)

The March 1864 flood invaded many town shops including those of the Maynes. It was heaviest in lower Albert Street as shown here. (Fryer Library, Browning Collection)

The April 1864 Queen Street fire. Nineteen looters were arrested. Mayne's home was spared. (Fryer Library, Alcock Slide Collection)

The 1872 Brisbane Grammar School football team. William Mayne (rear second from right) looks remarkably like his father. (Brisbane Grammar School Archives)

S.S. *Walrus*. The floating sugar mill rumoured to be the scene of Isaac Mayne's gambling parties and a murder. (Fryer Library, Browning Collection)

Mary Emelia Mayne. At nineteen she was wilful and rebellious with little outlet for teenage self-expression. (University of Queensland Archives)

Dr James Mayne, aged 38, when he was Superintendent of Brisbane General Hospital. (1898–1904). (University of Queensland Archives)

"Moorlands", built 1892. It was a gracious home but no "Garden of Eden" for the family. (Drawn by Val Webb. Courtesy of Wesley Hospital.)

The staircase in "Moorlands" was designed for the redemption of Patrick's soul. (Drawn by Max Brewer)

Dr Ernest Sandford Jackson, the surgeon who regarded James as the best assistant surgeon he ever had. (Brisbane Hospital *Monthly Chronicle*, c.1910)

Dr F.W. (Fred) Whitehouse (lower right) coach of the Church of England Grammar School Rowing Team, 1949. As a young student he was befriended by James. They remained life-long companions. (Fryer Library)

St Lucia area in the 1930s where James, and Fred Whitehouse strolled and dreamed of a noble university rising on the farmland. (University of Queensland Archives. Original by *Courier-Mail*)

James Mayne Cottage at Pt Lookout, North Stradbroke Island. His gift to an amateur fishermen's group. Demolished 1995. (Courtesy Barbara Widdup)

James in the 1930s. His style of dressing was distinctly that of a Londoner. Note the boutonnaire, gloves, cane and diamond pin. (Courtesy Noel Haysom)

James inspecting the site of the St Lucia land with the Lord Mayor, Alderman William Jolly. 16 May 1930. (University of Queensland Archives)

James and Mary Mayne at the laying of the foundation stone for the Forgan Smith Building at St Lucia. 6 March 1937. The once wilful beauty was barely aware of her surroundings. Note her symbolic winged heart brooch and her diamond bracelet. (University of Queensland Archives. Original, *Daily Telegraph*)

Melville Haysom's 1936 portrait of Dr James Mayne in ermine-trimmed robes holding a map of the proposed new site for the University of Queensland

A young Dr Fred Whitehouse with Prof. H. C. Richards, head of the Geology department, at a graduation long before Fred's dismissal in 1955 (courtesy Peg Martin née Richards)

The Mayne family on holiday in New Zealand, pictured with Florence Davidson, taken in 1897. (Back row, from left) Mary Emelia Mayne, Florence Davidson, William Mayne, Mr Stewart, (front row, from left) James Mayne, Isaac Mayne (courtesy Jill Bruxner)

Various members of the travelling party seen here with the "bone-shaking" coach. Mary Emelia (in dark suit), Florence Davidson, William (seated in coach on right), Mr Stewart (in top hat) (courtesy Jill Bruxner)

A lost love? ... Florence Davidson and William Mayne. "The diary is eloquently silent on their parting."

human problems of his colonial flock, would have discussed that problem with the attending doctor and then talked over the prospects of the family's future with Mary. It is possible that both of them suspected the beginnings of a problem with Rosanna. Dunne would undoubtedly have backed Mary in convincing her children of a sensible decision. The two eldest were well into puberty, old enough and intelligent enough to take part in any family discussion. Assuming that Mary was ignorant of the murder until Patrick's confession, she would have been horrified by her recently acquired knowledge and saddened by grief and malicious whispers; but she was strong enough to understand and act on what she considered best for her family. She was a Protestant; Father Dunne was a valuable friend and counsellor; she was capable of issuing the advice not to marry and hoping that her children would comply.

The actual crime and the names of the two victims, Cox and Fyfe, unknown to most, were forgotten quite early. The name of Patrick Mayne, the murderer, was not forgotten. Had any of the children ever contemplated marriage, the wild distorted versions of his many supposed crimes that exist to this day were waiting to engulf them. They grew up painfully aware of that circumstance.

For Mary, those troubled August days were rapidly overtaken by a different despair. She was faced with bequests totalling £400 for Patrick's brother and three sisters, wages to be paid to thirteen men, two girls and the nurse; burned and damaged buildings still needing costly repairs so they could again earn rent, and a mountain of debts and some dishonoured cheques which confirmed the grim prospect of bankruptcy. There was £700.12.6d. in the bank and £20,258.5.11d. owing to other people. The largest debt was to the Bank of New South Wales. It had been negotiated by Patrick in 1860 at the high interest rate of 13 per cent and was secured by the bank holding the title deeds of several choice pieces of his real estate. McLean and Best were owed £2,000 for cattle, and £1,500 was still unpaid on Moggill farm. The interest payments alone were crippling.

Mary had kept things going through the last months of her husband's illness, but what lay ahead was another matter. Neither she nor Patrick had ever been the type to remain unnoticed. Like him, she was quite capable of sending gossips packing with a flea in their ear. Now her situation was different. She was very much in the public eye, an object of more serious public speculation. It would have been easy for an uneducated woman in mid-life with all her domestic responsibilities to sell sufficient property to pay the debts and find a nice little house in the suburbs. She stood to inherit £300 a year; all the rest was for the children. If the end result of selling meant that her money was reduced, she would not have been wealthy but she would have been very comfortably off, with sufficient money to educate her five children and a fair inheritance preserved for their adult years.

The alternative was years of hard work, both mental and physical, to keep things going on a more businesslike and long-term basis. She was untrained and would need to learn rapidly how to cope with accounts and workmen, tenants of farms and buildings, contractors and bankers — people who had contempt for women such as she. The tiger in Mary had no intention of failing her cubs. Life with Patrick had accustomed her to living with a high degree of uncertainty; she had learned to tolerate the unfamiliar. She rearranged her life and, with valuable advice from the experienced Raff and Darragh, began what turned out to be a bigger struggle than any of them could have anticipated.

It was not just a matter of learning how Patrick had done things. In 1866, the year following his death, business confidence gave way to alarm about the future. When some of the London banks collapsed, the waves of failure swept across Australia. The Bank of Queensland closed in July 1866. This was followed by the failure of the Queensland Steam Navigation Company in which Patrick had invested heavily. His own financial collapse had been a forerunner to several high-flyers' insolvencies. Even Bishop Quinn struggled under a debt of some £10,000, also borrowed at a high rate, much of it to purchase the mansion "Adderton" for a convent.

Among the middle-class investors and businessmen claimed by insolvency were five aldermen. Unpaid in their civic role, they had to resign their seats to salvage what was left in the worsening economic climate. Gold fever had beguiled many men into believing that a bonanza would vindicate their property gamble. Instead, as unemployment grew, land values dropped. At a time when new bright gas lights were being installed in Brisbane town, business was becoming dimmed everywhere. All traders found their takings severely reduced.

It was expected that Mary would sell enough of their real estate to meet the debt. Had she done so in those depression years, sales at bargain prices would have materially diminished the interests of the inheritors, her children. Reluctantly she faced the fact that Rosevale Station, at least two days' ride distant, three days with a dray, was too far away for her to supervise. It had to be let go early and cheaply. She sold it to Morts for £2,321.14.9d. and the stock for another £1,500, and reduced the debt to the bank. In 1868, when the troubled bank decided to foreclose, Mary and her co-trustees applied to the Supreme Court to see if she had the power under Patrick's will to raise a mortgage on enough of the properties to discharge all of his debt. Interest rates had dropped to considerably less than the 13 per cent they were paying to the bank; a new mortgage seemed a reasonable financial solution to satisfy all parties. The Chief Justice, His Honour Mr James Cockle, consented to their request, and the Anglican Bishop of Brisbane, E.W. Tufnell, came to her aid, lending her £4,000 at an interest of $3^3/_4$ per cent. Five months later, on 26 April 1869, Mary's letter to the Court reads:

> As executrix, I have taken the entire management of the administration of the said estate and I did, out of my own funds and other moneys which I have borrowed from time to time, pay off and discharge the debts due, and that the balance of accounts is now due to me by the estate of the said Patrick Mayne for and on account of moneys paid by me to the creditors.

Those five months had seen a new legal setback. George Raff was having troubles. He worked some sixty to a hundred Melanesians on his plantation "Morayfield" at Caboolture, and was an active defender of the Kanaka labour system, against the growing moral concern of what some, especially the clergy, called slave labour. Although a number of Raff's Kanakas absconded and he took sixteen of them to court, he was investigated, cleared, and declared a good employer. He was influential but unpopular. The failure of the Q.S.N. Company was time-consuming and the prolonged political controversy over the Kanakas was damaging to his political career. When Mary was given permission to mortgage more property to try to trade the estate out of debt, Raff decided to withdraw as an executor and trustee for the Mayne children. He needed time and energy to shore up his finances, popularity, and political chances.

The Maynes had never been socially accepted. The murky stories about Patrick were always high on the gossip list, and finding a reputable replacement who would shoulder considerable responsibility was difficult. In February 1869 the surprise acceptance was that of John Petrie, civic-minded, but no friend of the Maynes. It is tempting to think that his acceptance was a tribute to Mary's ability to cope; but more likely the initiator was the new mortgagee, Bishop Tufnell who, with his own building plans for the future, would gain some leverage with John Petrie and his contracting firm.

For a short period Mary thought she could now live as a private person away from the stress and shame. She left her employees to continue the smooth running of the shop and took the children to live at Sandgate, by now a fashionable holiday area for moneyed people. James' joyous memories of running barefoot in the sand and of it being "the happiest time of his life" are all that is known of that time. No doubt for the seven-year-old boy and his nine-year-old sister, the warmth of their mother's care and attention and the freedom of a bigger playground than dung-strewn, dusty Queen Street made that time more precious. But Mary found that making frequent long carriage rides from Sandgate to attend to business in town was impractical and they returned to Queen Street.

By 1874 prices were on the rise again. After seven years of being a butcher, Mary had sold the business in 1872. Now was a good time to think about shedding a little more property in order to make a large dint in the remaining debt. With no more need for cattleyards and shepherds at the Mayne estate, she sold part of that land, an allotment in Leichhardt Street and another in William Street for £4,446.6.0. The rest of the estate was intact. The family could afford to relax a little. Rosanna, now twenty-five and about to enter a convent, was able to draw £500 as an advance from her share of the estate.

Apart from the neatly compiled statements rendered to the Court, there is nothing else to tell us of the tremendous effort made by the former servant girl to save the fortune which ultimately paid for both the St Lucia site and the Moggill Farm of the University of Queensland, and which still provides continuous funds for its Faculty of Medicine. In December 1879, fourteen years after Patrick died, the last account was fully paid and the estate cleared. There is nothing to tell us if Mary attacked her formidable task with the same belligerence that saw her tie up her neighbour's chickens and defend her action with a fence post — or whether, fifteen years after that imbroglio, she had become a mature negotiator. To keep going for fourteen vigilant years after Patrick's death to trade away the debt would have demanded all her determination and zealous enthusiasm. It may be that long experience of coping with Patrick's exaggerated mood changes had taught her strategies for success. Of her personal life in that time, there are only two clues: repairs to a house at Sandgate in which we know she holidayed with the children for a short time, and a bill for £15 for sherry. Both are from 1866; both probably eased the stress so that she could carry on.

8

Out of the Ashes

IT is fair to say that Patrick's widow, Mary McIntosh Mayne, was the unsung hero of the family, the woman whose efforts the ultimate beneficiary, the University of Queensland, might recognise. She inherited no property; the only tangible remnant of her life is a neat, regular signature on her will and on the accounts rendered to the Court at the end of her long labour to save the estate. Not even a photograph of her exists. If James and Mary were any indication, her children were relatively handsome, but whether she is reflected in their strong faces and wide-set eyes, we cannot know.

Buoyed up with news of Patrick's success in Australia, his sister Rosa, to whom he had left £100, decided to try her luck in Brisbane. In the early 1840s she had left

County Tyrone for New York, married Joseph Mooney and borne several children. The family's arrival in 1866 was probably at Mary's suggestion; soon the Mooneys became licensees paying rent to the Mayne estate for the Royal Exchange Hotel at the corner of Albert and Elizabeth Streets. It is doubtful whether the two families could have maintained more than a kin relationship, for when Joseph died in 1871, Rosa continued to rent and run the hotel while raising their seven children. She would have had as little time for social life as the fully occupied Mary. What Rosa did display was the same strength and drive as that of her brother, Patrick. Both Patrick's sisters, Ann and Rosa, were close enough to Mary to witness her signature on her will, but the young Mooneys' lives took different paths from that of their wealthy and well-educated cousins. Aunt Ann Mayne, for whom Mary, and then her children, always assumed a responsibility, probably maintained the family contact. For forty-three years she lived as a helpful and welcome member in the Mayne household, but after her death the Mooneys do not appear to have been among the visitors to "Moorlands".

Four of Mary's children, like their parents, were achievers. Rosanna at All Hallows' was doing very well, particularly in music and French. In 1866 the only further education available for teenage boys came from one of about two dozen townsfolk with varying standards of education who advertised classes in their homes for a shilling a week. The Reverend B.G. Shaw's Collegiate School, conducted in his home "Alexandra" on Wickham Terrace, was selected for Isaac; here he eventually passed an examination which led to employment as a clerk with Queen Street solicitor Thomas Bunton. Fr Dunne's protective eye was never far away from the Mayne children, and his night school for boys no doubt also contributed to Isaac's further education so that he was able to be articled to Bunton in 1871. The bright but younger William and James were yet to prove themselves.

A factor in the shaping of Rosanna's life was the extension of the work of the Sisters of Mercy to the Darling Downs. The 1860s depression years had seen migrants and labourers moving west in search of a better life on the fertile western plains, their move made easier by the opening of the Ipswich to Toowoomba railway line in 1867. Among them were a large number of Bishop Quinn's migrants whom he sponsored under his Queensland Immigration Society. They began filling the open spaces in the Toowoomba district. It was the largest settled area west of the ranges and its 3,000 settlers were in need of a permanent service for their religious life, and education for their children.

Fr Dunne, who had frequent differences with his authoritarian bishop, James Quinn, was despatched west to succour and guide Toowoomba's largely Irish and German Catholic population. His going was a loss to Mary Mayne; while she struggled to run the butchery and worried about the large debt, he had kept an eye on Rosanna, who was boarding at All Hallows' convent. The girl was high-spirited, with rapid changes of mood; with other promising senior students she was training as a pupil-teacher, but both Dunne and Mary knew she had ideas of becoming a nun. Dunne was also aware of the strains caused by the hard life, long hours and poor food, which were the lot of the pioneering Sisters of Mercy. They accepted their life but too much was expected of them; already the ranks of the younger nuns were being depleted by a high death rate from tuberculosis and exhaustion. Dunne's own sister in Ireland had succumbed to what we would now see as overwork and neglect by her superiors. He was also acutely aware that in the cloistered life of Brisbane, as in any community of strong-minded people, there were clashes of personalities which could be unsettling to the most vulnerable in the community. A current problem was a difference of view between the Bishop and some of the Sisters of Mercy. There were, in fact, pro- and anti-Quinn factions; in 1868, this had resulted in a rebellion by two sisters who had walked out and boarded a ship for Sydney.

In an effort to make Rosanna aware of the reality of religious life, the demands that would be put on her and the responsibility of the vows she would take, Dunne wrote to her from Toowoomba giving the example of what had happened to the two rebel sisters. He told her that to avoid a scandal he had been sent to the ship to make the rebels' trip look like Bishop's business. He was instructed to point out to them the illegality of their leaving, and to bring them back. Although the two women had the sympathy of several members of the Australian Catholic

Church hierarchy, their fate on returning to Brisbane was more than admonishment. Mother McDermott was stripped of her authority and her companion rebel, Sister Cecelia McAuliffe, who was not strong enough to stand the stress, died within six months.

Whether or not Rosanna gave any further thought to the serious matter of taking vows, the subject was dropped for some time.

Mary's attention had to centre more positively on the future of her sons. The replacement executor and trustee, John Petrie, was enrolling his son at the new Brisbane Grammar School at Roma Street. So was George Raff, the former executor. Apart from Petrie's role as executor and guardian of the Mayne children, Mary had also employed his company to rebuild fire-damaged buildings. No doubt, with sons of similar age, they found time to discuss their lads' futures. Along with the Petrie and Raff boys, William Mayne was among the first pupils enrolled at the Brisbane Grammar School in 1869.

Schooldays at Grammar opened a window on a different world. William began mixing with the sons of privileged and socially accepted families, something new to the Maynes, who were not socially accepted. He discovered acceptance in the world of sport with its nineteenth-century public school gentleman's code; without neglecting his studies he quickly shone at cricket and football. He played in the school teams for both sports, and in 1875 captained the cricket team. At Grammar, William began to shed some of the rough edges that had pervaded family life under Patrick's rule. Accustomed to money, he had no real difficulty in fitting into a new life and absorbing what was then seen as the ideal of a public school boy. In a short time he was on the way to becoming the cultivated gentleman that was the man.

By 1871, with Isaac articled to the solicitor Thomas Bunton for a fee of £105 a year, Rosanna a pupil-teacher (one of the few positions open to a colonial gentlewoman), and William being educated alongside the sons of the colony's best families, Mary had cause to feel some satisfaction with her dual role as mother and businesswoman. Such satisfaction would have been a little dimmed by the end of the year, however. Thirteen-year-old Mary Emelia, who displayed neither drive nor ambition, was removed from All Hallows'. It was recommended that as she had no taste whatever for study, she should follow domestic pursuits. With no need to work and too much time on her hands, the attractive, non-studious teenager was regarded as "flighty". It was a time when her mother was fully involved in trying to save the children's inheritance; even had there been time to devote to her daughter, the society for which they were financially eligible remained uninterested in opening its ranks to the Maynes. The environment of dusty, still down-at-heel Queen Street was no place for such a vulnerable young girl. At the end of a wasted year it seems her mother must have forgotten bluster and mustered considerable tact, for both her daughter and the redoubtable Mother Bridget Conlan were persuaded to try again. At the beginning of 1873, young Mary Emelia was packed back to All Hallows', this time as a boarder, and remained there until she was nineteen. Her rebellious nature was not fully subdued but she was destined to spend the rest of her life doing as she was told.

Unfortunately for her mother's peace of mind, almost immediately the high-strung Rosanna's sense of vocation surfaced again. On 4 March 1873, Fr Dunne once more wrote from Toowoomba, saying that he believed that "a lay woman could answer the call of holiness through teaching, daily prayer, spiritual reading and works of charity, without having to take religious vows". His doubts were well-founded. On one occasion, as a pupil-teacher at All Hallows', Rosanna failed to take a class and gave no reason for her absence. When it was discovered that she had gone to the races at Ipswich, Mother Bridget's reprimand was sharp and to the point. She warned Rosanna "that she was drifting rapidly, and explained to what". For the culprit it was probably an echo of those wild impulses that drove her father to some of his actions. It was a portent of what was to come, and Robert Dunne sensed this. His cautionary letter to Rosanna had little effect. She became a novice at All Hallows' Convent, and within three months was a pawn in a new clash between Father Dunne and Bishop Quinn. The Bishop was backed by his protégé, Mother Bridget Conlan, who had earlier replaced the rebel Mother McDermott as Reverend Mother.

The clash in 1873 was over a little group of sisters who were to be sent to Toowoomba to set up a new centre.

They were to live at St Saviour's, a rented house in James Street, and they were expected to earn money both by teaching at the new St Patrick's School and taking in students as boarders. They were also to open an orphanage, an asylum for needy women, and to act as hospital and gaol visitors. Dunne had very definite ideas about education. He believed that the ideal Catholic school was one in which a nun's religious vocation and her role as a Catholic educator were clearly differentiated. This he perceived to be a great flaw in the convent system. When he learned of the proposed transfer of nuns, he stood his own ground as much as he could and claimed the right to regulate and direct the work of the sisters according to his judgment. Only then would he accept a situation for which he had not asked and which was thrust on him by Bishop Quinn. The nuns at All Hallows' Convent were aware of Dunne's attitudes. No sisters volunteered to go to Toowoomba and those nominated begged not to be sent.

In July, Mother Rose Flanagan, Sister Evangelist Kearney, and the postulant, Rosanna Mayne, arrived in Toowoomba. The surprise inclusion was Rosanna. It was most unusual in those times for a postulant to be sent to the founding of a new centre, and most unwise to send a girl with her unpredictable temperament. Dunne made it known that they would be permitted to teach on a trial basis only. They would work under the direction of the lay head teacher, Kate Reordan, and there would be no review of the situation until the sisters had demonstrated their ability to cope with the schoolwork. Apart from Dunne's concern for the mental health of twenty-three year old Rosanna, he knew that the load which all the Toowoomba sisters were trying to carry was far too heavy. Rosanna was still training as a pupil-teacher, and among her extra duties she was required to give music lessons. It left her too little time to study for the Board of General Education Examinations. She was not coping very well and Dunne, knowing her family history, worried about possible consequences of nervous strain which might result from overwork. Much more was expected of the sisters than of the rural priests, and within a few months the health of Mother Rose, the Superior at Toowoomba, was also causing concern. Dunne believed that in this situation, not enough attention could be given to Rosanna's needs. His concern was such that after watching her for fifteen months, he wrote to her mother advising her to get a court order, if necessary, to remove Rosanna from the convent in Toowoomba.

During nine years of problems and decision-making, Mary had learned to exercise control over her affairs. It had fortified her to handle emergencies and deal with people in authority in a very able manner. She was well able to speak for herself. This crisis was far more serious than getting Mary Emelia re-enrolled at school. Rosanna was the responsibility of the Sisters of Mercy. Mary's determination, set against the heavy-handed Bishop Quinn and the austere Mother Bridget Conlan, is indicated by the fact that Rosanna was quickly returned to All Hallows' in Brisbane, where she was given a lighter load, teaching music and general subjects to the sisters. Dunne's belief that the novice needed a quieter environment was proved correct. For some years her strong religious conviction and her calm life within the religious order in Brisbane held her darker forces at bay.

It is typical of the times that although Fr Dunne's letter was addressed to Mrs Mayne, it is everywhere accepted and written that "Rosie was transferred at the request of her father who was one of the most influential Catholic business men in Brisbane". He had been dead for nine years.

During this period of her eldest daughter's difficulty, Mary had sold the butchery, but the family remained in their Queen Street home adjoining the shop. It was large, brick, comfortable and central. Like Patrick, Mary had preferred to work from the hub of things. Now she had more time for her children, but during those earlier, more difficult years, the eldest three had been busy building their own lives. Isaac, twenty-two and man of the house, had high hopes of getting approval for registration as a solicitor, Rosanna was soon to be professed as a nun with the Sisters of Mercy, William, with good scholastic results, had plans to further his education at the University of Sydney. The household had shrunk to Mary, her sister-in-law Ann Mayne and her three sons. Only young James still needed her supervision. Patrick's estate was not yet finalised. The rents, property maintenance and the debt repayment were time-consuming, but without the shop, the load was a great deal lighter. It was time for a change.

Queen Street was no longer suitable for Mary or the children's future.

There were several rented houses in Patrick's estate, and in 1874 Mary decided to move the family to one of them at Milton, where the estate held quite a lot of land. None of it had a river frontage, but with the rapid expansion of Brisbane, Milton was a coming suburb. Several very substantial homes were being erected in the area. Some of the Mayne land had been intersected by resumptions for the new Brisbane to Ipswich railway line. It is possible they moved to the hill behind their river-fronted neighbours, John Markwell and the Kents, who rented grazier J.F. McDougall's two-storied "Milton House". McDougall's land stretched almost from Cribb Street, Milton, to what is now Chasely Street, Auchenflower. Markwell, a Queen Street ironmonger, owned a charming low-set bungalow with wide shady verandas around which spread a wilderness of shrubs and flowers. It was called "Moorlands Villa", and his land stretched upstream from Chasely Street to the shallow Langsville Creek, which meandered by what is now Patrick Lane, Toowong.

The move to Milton was probably about mid-year, for, at the beginning of the third term, Mary's youngest child, the quiet, introspective twelve-year-old James, finished at St Stephen's primary school and joined his brother at Brisbane Grammar. Unlike William, James did not excel at sport. He quietly got on with his studies and left no mark of his passing.

Life settled into some sort of normalcy at Milton and

by late 1877 the end of all their financial problems was in sight. There was, however, no end to their other problem. Although Patrick's death was well behind them, the public memory of his life still imposed an undeclared persecution. With the building of the new St Stephen's Cathedral in 1875, Mary had offered reparation for her husband's sins by donating one of the beautiful stained-glass windows on the side wall. A memorial to Patrick, it portrays a fallen soldier at the feet of a merciful Christ. But that gift made no difference to people's attitude. The innocent members of the family continued to pay a price. Whispered stories were kept alive and the family drew in on itself. To this day, the aging offspring of old-timers still say: "Oh yes, I remember that family. We knew they were there, but we wouldn't have taken tea with them." Some even point out that it was not for reasons of class; among those they called on was a successful family of O'Sheas whose pioneering mother was a washerwoman.

The Maynes had a justifiable pride in achievement, and out of that grew a quiet dignity, a tangible barrier with a soft gentleness which has been a remembered quality in the three youngest. It hid a lot of unhappiness, but was so well disciplined that it remained intact through all the horror that was to come. There was little hint of this in 1877. Rosanna was professed as a nun at All Hallows', taking the name of Sister Mary Mel. Isaac had been registered as a solicitor the year before and remained with his employer, Thomas Bunton, in Queen Street. William was in his second year of an Arts course at the University of

Sydney, and at nineteen, Mary Emelia had absorbed as much education as she found interesting and was allowed to leave school. She was tall, with a lively, wide-eyed, open face, full of life and restless. Their mother, with more time on her hands than she had ever had before, was bored with suburbia. The isolation and discrimination had barely impinged on her busy life as a butcher; now it became obvious. She was fifty-seven, independent and hard-working; like Patrick, she did not take kindly to being slighted. Thanks to the way she had kept the business going, since 1868, they had each drawn a living allowance. Those who could get away would now travel to Europe. They were Mary, Patrick's sister Ann Mayne, young Mary Emelia, and Isaac, who was quite happy to take leave and escort them. James was at a crucial stage of his secondary education, so at the beginning of 1878 he was transferred from Brisbane Grammar School to board at the Catholic St Killian's College at South Brisbane. It was regarded as the right school for boys who were likely prospects for the priesthood, and to that end he studied history, geography, French and Latin. The arrangement was also convenient for his Catholic guardian, Joseph Darragh of Kangaroo Point, whose eldest son joined the holiday-makers as a companion for Isaac.

On 28 March 1878, they sailed for Marseilles on the R.M.S. *Bowen*. It was not a very large ship (884 tons) and had only three other European passengers. It was, however, crammed with a large number of Chinese returning to Singapore and Hong Kong via four northern

Queensland ports and Thursday Island. Their exodus was due, no doubt, to the new Chinese Immigration Act and the Gold Fields Amendment Act, brought in when it was realised that on the Palmer goldfields in North Queensland there were 17,000 Chinese, outnumbering Europeans by twelve to one. For the Maynes it was a sensible choice of ship. It gave them an opportunity to experience something of the Orient, and avoided the popular ships which took the southern route to England and were patronised by those whose gossip could have dampened the family'spleasure.

Those few months before they sailed were the last time the entire family was to have much time together. In 1879, once the debt was cleared and the estate could be finalised, the young adult Maynes began receiving their inheritance of property. Good regular rents allowed the boys to step out into the world. William lived comfortably in Sydney, later to be joined by James. After gaining his Bachelor of Arts degree, William remained in Sydney to study for a Master's degree. He was still there when James arrived in 1880. Both graduated in 1884, at which time James left for postgraduate study at University College Hospital in London. At home, Isaac assumed nominal headship of the family, but it was a home dominated by two women, his mother, and Aunt Ann, and disturbed by the frustrated wilfulness of Mary Emelia. Nevertheless, it was to Isaac that Fr Dunne wrote when next he tried to help Rosanna.

Dunne's troubles with Bishop Quinn came to a head in 1880, when the Bishop chose to interpret an application for holiday leave as a resignation. Protests failed, so on 11 March 1881 Dunne sailed for London. Although he had worked in Toowoomba for more than twelve years, he had not forgotten his pastoral care of several of his earlier charges, including the Maynes. He still corresponded with them. Rosanna's state of mental health in 1881 is not known, but Dunne and her family were well aware of its continued fragility. While in Sydney, on board ship, and in Ireland, he kept in contact with her, bolstering her spirit and suggesting ways of living a calm life. In some half-dozen letters to her he wrote of the contemplative life of nineteenth-century monks and their detachment from material things. He noted a similar detachment in good missionaries, and from Dublin he described how he found the genuine joy of monastic solitude at Mt Melleray Abbey.

During his travels he was never far from news of Queensland. He was saddened by Bishop Quinn's illness and death in August, and disturbed by news that some Brisbane Sisters of Mercy might be sent hundreds of miles north to the fledgling see of Rockhampton. On 8 September he wrote two letters, one to Rosanna explaining some difficulties in the secular life in Brisbane, and a second to her brother, Isaac, warning him that if young Brisbane Sisters of Mercy were sent to Rockhampton and the

Queensland diocese was subsequently divided, they would be lost to Brisbane forever. Isaac acted on the warning. Rosanna (Sister Mary Mel) was not in the contingent that went to Rockhampton.

Robert Dunne's subsequent return to Queensland in March 1882 to become the new Bishop of Brisbane was a source of satisfaction to Mary. The now financially and intellectually independent Maynes no longer needed him, but the valuable friendship remained. Despite the fact that her children were staunch, church-going Catholics, Protestant Mary never converted to their faith. That was no reflection on her high regard for Bishop Dunne. She admired him and respected his wise and comforting advice. At All Hallows', Rosanna's mental health began a sharp decline, with an intermittent need to control her in a strait-jacket. At such times, Dunne's compassion must have gone a long way to easing Mary's mind about her daughter's welfare. In the light of Patrick's psychopathic behaviour, Rosanna's future was cause for considerable anxiety. No longer able to teach, she was relieved of that work; on her good days she was allowed to act as secretary to Mother Vincent. Those good days were to become fewer and farther apart.

In October 1881, their fifty-eight year old neighbour, John Markwell, had died and when his widow Harriet put the river-fronted "Moorlands Villa" up for sale, the Maynes purchased it. The house had a sad history. Markwell married three times. The house was a wedding gift to him and his second wife Georgina. She and three of her children died early. Two children died at ten months, one at fifteen months, a seven-year-old was drowned, and one daughter did not survive her twelfth year. The sixth, his eldest son, Henry John Markwell, managed to reach twenty-three before he was fatally thrown from his galloping horse. The coming of the Maynes to River Road did not end the tragedy attached to that apparently charming garden of Eden. Instead, the name Markwell eventually became intricately entangled in the complex Mayne family myth.

After the move, Mary dropped from recorded view. Owning no property in her own right, she features only once in a Post Office directory. Isaac's name now appears with the address River Road, Toowong. It would be imagining the inconsistent to expect that a woman of Mary's strength and temperament spent all her time quietly but happily, in her pleasant garden with the company of her sister-in-law and some of her children. Having exercised command in her world for eighteen years, she was unlikely now to take a back seat. There is more reason to believe that her authority was never surrendered to any of her sons. It was a women's household in which Isaac lived and to which William returned, aged twenty-eight. In 1884 he came home from Sydney University with a Master of Arts degree, a gentleman's style, a taste for good jewellery, and no apparent inclination to do other than live on the money he had inherited. He allowed himself to become a Commissioner of the Peace, which no doubt was useful in witnessing signatures in the various family property deals.

The outgoing young sportsman of Grammar School days had drained his small cup of social freedom. Coming home, he faced social stigma because of his father's crime. The gentleman's clubs which might have rounded out the style of life he desired were not open to him. He, too, withdrew and became locked into a very private life. Local folklore agrees that he was an excellent horseman, a skill he had learned from Patrick in the 1860s. Until old age he rode regularly in solitude in the western suburbs. He still kept a horse at "Moorlands" at the time of his death.

Despite the Maynes' low profile, the family shame was never allowed to be buried by the passage of time. In 1888, Henry Stuart Russell's book *The Genesis of Queensland* retold the gruesome story of the Cox murder. No doubt the fact that Isaac Mayne was a solicitor stayed the author's pen from actually naming Patrick as the murderer, but he ended the chapter by writing:

> the cook was charged with the crime, tried, convicted and hung, in spite of loud protestations of innocence. Some years afterwards another, in the horror of a deathbed upbraiding, confessed that he had been the guilty one, and had looked on at the execution of his innocent *locum tenens*! Let his name perish!

Brisbane people avidly read this popular history of their State. The reborn tragedy ensured that the family had little peace. Its effect on them, particularly on the ageing Mary, was incalculable. On 3 September 1889 she suffered a heart attack and died. If her immigration papers are correct, she was sixty-eight, not sixty-three as stated on her death certificate. Although she remained a Protestant, she was buried high on a hill in the Irish Catholic section of the Toowong cemetery by her long-time friend, the Catholic Archbishop of Brisbane, Robert Dunne.

Three weeks after her funeral the remains of Patrick, whose deathbed confession twenty-four years earlier had laid an unending burden on the family, was disinterred from the cemetery at Milton and reburied beside her. With him went their baby daughter Evelina Selina, who died in 1854; and Mary's mother, Mary Kelly. No record tells us whether this was Mary's wish for the family to be together or whether Isaac and William decided that their removal was necessary.

At that time it was not unusual for bodies to be moved from Milton; the area was prone to flooding. In the late 1850s a large section of nearby land had been Patrick's bullock paddock, watered by the run-off from Paddington heights and had a six foot deep water hole. The poorly drained cemetery was also subject to flooding and it was not unknown for coffins to float. These occurences led to renewed gossip, making it very stressful for the already overburdened Mary and her children.

From 1875 when Milton was closed some families had their loved-one's coffins removed to a better-drained cemetery. Hundreds of graves without a headstone could not be identified and the neglected site became an eyesore. In an effort to tidy it up, unclaimed, smashed headstones were crushed and used for landfill. When Patrick was moved to Toowong cemetery the headstone remained and, with Mary Kelly's, was one of a few shifted up to the Presbyterian section on the highest, driest ground where they are today. The low flat sandstone tablet that marked Irish Catholic Patrick's grave is with those of some of John Dunmore Lang's Presbyterian citizens of note. It no longer marks his grave, but Patrick would have greatly relished being of historic importance, renowned not for his crime, but for being a member of Brisbane's first town council.

9

A Family Ostracised

AS far as can be ascertained, Isaac was thirty-six before he stepped sufficiently out of line to attract adverse notice. In April 1888, a Mrs Mary Kelly called on her solicitor, Thomas Bunton to make her will. Although she had the same name as Isaac's maternal grandmother, she was not related — one of the many Mary Kellys in Queensland. A countrywoman, she owned several properties, some in Brisbane, and as her only child had died, she planned to leave her estate to her several grandchildren. Three executors were to hold the properties in trust until the children came of age, and act as their guardians. Two executors were from Dalby; the third was the solicitor, Isaac Mayne. Mrs Kelly died on 28 September 1889; four days later, Isaac's employer, Thomas Bunton filed with the

Supreme Court a renunciation of Isaac's role as executor and guardian. In it Isaac declared:

> that he had not intermeddled in the personal estate and effects of the said deceased and will not hereafter intermeddle therein with intent to defraud Creditors and I do hereby appoint Thomas Bunton of Brisbane aforesaid my Proctor Solicitor and Attorney to file or cause to be filed this renunciation for me in the said registry of the said Supreme Court of Queensland.

This was just a month after his own mother had died. Her will, drawn up in 1878, two days before their overseas trip, when Isaac was the only adult son in Brisbane, discriminated against her daughters. It left Rosanna (Sister Mary Mel) £25 to buy a souvenir, Mary Emelia £50, and Patrick's sister Ann Mayne £500. All Mary's real and personal estate, valued at £16,000 was left to the three boys, Isaac, William and James.

Neither Patrick nor Mary had seen a need to share much of their wealth with their churches. His only sizeable donation had been £50 in 1864 for Bishop Quinn's Cathedral Fund. After Patrick died, Protestant Mary had done her duty by giving St Stephen's the costly stained-glass window as a memorial for her husband. Neither willed any money to their respective churches. Mary's will clearly indicated that none of her money was to go to the Sisters of Mercy through her daughter Rosanna. She was of the opinion that Rosanna's ample share of her father's will made sufficient provision for her dowry. Although the other daughter, Mary Emelia lived with her brothers, she, too, was effectively cut out of her mother's will. If Mary Mayne was influenced in the disposition of her property, it could only have been by her solicitor son, Isaac. William either did not approve of the unequal distribution or, at a later stage, had feelings of guilt about it. His will rectified the unequal position by making provision for Mary Emelia with a special bequest of £5,000 to be paid immediately before his estate was divided equally between her and James.

At the time of his mother's death James was still studying in London. He did not return until 1891. The boy who had lived away from home since boarding-school days in 1878 was now a man of thirty. He came home to a very changed household. Mary Emelia was thirty-two, full-bosomed and tall, but still undecided on how to spell her own name. Sometimes she called herself Emelia, sometimes Amelia; on some documents she used both spellings. Her brothers considered her flighty, and at times they locked her in her room, from where even distant neighbours could hear her loud continued protests.

Isaac was moody and tending to stoutness. Having little interest in anything apart from the law, he lacked the cultivated style of the more widely-educated William and James. According to the few who remember William, he was a gentleman with a known interest in the classics, a knowledge which later probably influenced a great deal of the interior decoration of "Moorlands". James, like Isaac, was shorter than Mary Emelia. He remained quiet and reserved with gracious manners. His London style of dressing hinted at an interest in fashion. He usually wore a bowler hat, flourished a silk paisley handkerchief in his breast pocket and quite frequently livened up his spirits by sporting a bright *boutonnière.* On special occasions he gave his delight in beautiful things a freer run, and often anchored his conservative choice of tie with a large diamond pin. After six years of medical training in Britain he had returned as a surgeon with higher qualifications than some of the handful of Brisbane doctors; nevertheless he did not attempt to set himself up as a private practitioner nor seek a partnership. Instead, he took up a less public role as a low-salaried resident medical officer at the Brisbane General Hospital. His appointment to the position brought the number of resident doctors to two, and soon he began building a Brisbane reputation as a skilled surgeon.

Both William and James had left the world of their Irish immigrant parents far behind. Both seemed gentle and lived a quiet, controlled way of life. They appear to have escaped the Mayne mental instability and exhibited nothing of Patrick's volatility or viciousness. Perhaps their lives, especially the stoicism they showed in coping with continued family tragedy, reflect the character of their mother. At the time of Patrick's death they were young enough to blot out his dubious role model; from then on the quality of Mary's mothering provided the security and stability that sustained them.

For James, the advantage of having lived for so long in

late nineteenth-century London's cultivated environment gave him a desire to maintain a similar cultured background in his life at home. William shared that interest — but the reality was that despite their wealth, style and education, all the Maynes' lives had a certain emptiness which was probably aggravated by the narrow confines of "Moorlands Villa", where all four had to work out their very different lives and temperaments. There was almost no outlet where they could relax and enjoy being part of a wider social group. They decided to build a grand new house with more space and a new environment to suit their tastes. In doing this they tried to blot out much of what had gone before and create the suggestion of a different past.

During the 1880s and 1890s, Brisbane took on a more substantial appearance. Prosperity was increasingly displayed in large elegant homes and imposing commercial buildings. No longer were the central Brisbane streets partly residential, and many inner-suburban dwellers were dispersing along the tram routes and railway lines. Toowong was an elite satellite suburb with shops, a hotel, churches, and a school. The Maynes engaged as their architect Richard Gailey, whose innovative designs and impressive buildings made him much sought after. His greatly admired Regatta Hotel already graced River Road. Built in 1886, he garlanded its three storeys with tiers of cast-iron lace balconies. "Moorlands", to be built in front of "Moorlands Villa", was to do equal justice to its designer.

This new residence was intended to mark the beginning of a new era for the family. On 2 June 1892, Mary Emelia was permitted to lay the foundation stone using a delicately embossed and inscribed silver trowel. On the site rose a large, two-storied mansion with an observation tower, from which they regularly flew the Union Jack. A charming combination of brick, timber and cast-iron, the house was set in acres of lawns, tall trees and gardens reaching back from River Road to the railway line at Auchenflower Station, halfway between Milton and Toowong.

The house was no sooner completed than the monsoon rains of February 1893 twice turned the river into a rampaging force that tore at riverside homes. The second flood savaged the trading heart of Brisbane and swept away much of the new Victoria Bridge. At the Regatta Hotel, just up the road from the Maynes' new home, two floors were invaded by swirling murky water. "Moorlands", on higher ground, safe above the thirty foot rise of the brown surging torrent, suffered only muddy lawns strewn with soggy, battered treasures washed from upstream people's lives.

Even today the grace and charm of "Moorlands" is still reasonably preserved. The interior is rich with the warm brown cedar of the staircase and wide folding doors. Several rooms have fireplace mantles of Italian marble. The dining room has dignified black marble, while all the other fireplace surrounds are soft, gleaming white. Elaborate detailing in gilded timber and ceramics enhanced the main rooms, while gas chandeliers hung from decorated plaster rosettes.

There was plenty of space here to be one's self. For the four Maynes and their aunt there were ten large rooms downstairs and ten bedrooms and several bathrooms above stairs. The most individual facet of their mansion is the large stained-glass window that dominates the entrance hall and sweeps upwards from the elaborately carved staircase to the high ceiling. The English influence on James' taste is clearly seen in the design of the window, which might have been found in many British homes reflecting a family's history. The design is built around eight delicate, pastel-coloured detailed cameos of two castles, two grand manor houses, and four seascapes. Linking them are the reeds, flowers, birds, butterflies and dragonflies of English moors, surmounted by two waterfowl.

In the angled staircase there is a strong statement of Catholic commitment. It is an act of propitiation by the family for the redemption of Patrick's soul. The four-sided newel post which faces everyone who enters the front door is topped by a solid orb and cross, the sign of the Church's domination of the world. Below it on each side is a carved rose, then the words *sursum corda* (lift up your hearts) from the beginning of the Mass. They surmount a winged heart, representing the assumption of the Virgin Mary into heaven. Around the base of the post are carved the initials "PM", and they are repeated on both sides of the twenty fretwork panels that reach up the staircase. It seems that the family adopted a special devotion to the Virgin; as patron saint of sinners, she was to intercede between Patrick and his God. The honour to their mother was kept quite separate. They were well aware of their debt to her, and at the time "Moorlands" was built, they financed another stained-glass memorial window in St Stephen's Cathedral in her memory. Near the entrance, its theme is Marian, again showing devotion to the Virgin.

James, particularly drawn to the Virgin Mary, was to adopt the winged heart and the motto *sursum corda* above his own entwined initials, as though it was an ancestral heraldic device. In gold, it decorates the blue suede cover of one of his photograph albums, and in 1936, the artist Melville Haysom incorporated it into James' portrait by adding the device to the plan of the University site which rests on his lap. James had a frequent need to lift up his heart. He was a sensitive, humane man, troubled by his family history and concerned by occasional signs that Isaac, like his father and sister Rosanna, might be carrying the hereditary flaw which governed their behaviour. Perhaps it was James who gave Mary Emelia her gold brooch which featured the device.

The building of "Moorlands" and the quiet, dignified life of the family gave a lift to their social acceptance. For a time, life moved comfortably within the limits which local approval accorded it. Colleagues of Isaac and James showed interest in the new home, and when it was completed the social pages noted that "Mary Emelia hosted a pleasant dance" in the ballroom. A month later they noted that she and Isaac travelled south for a holiday. This was one of the regular annual holidays which she took with Isaac. Sometimes they were accompanied by William, and on a few occasions all four went to New Zealand. Elderly Aunt Ann remained at home. She acted as housekeeper and companion to Mary Emelia, who, despite approaching middle age, never appears to have gone far from "Moorlands" without a brother as escort. One of her breaks from dull domesticity was church attendance. Regularly every Sunday two spirited horses, drawing a highly polished carriage with the morning sun gleaming on the spokes and harness, swept the family along River Road, Roma, George and Elizabeth Streets, to St Stephen's Cathedral.

Then, in 1895, rumour, dulled for a few years, began to fly as fast as their horses. It was sourced by another much-read book, J.J. Knight's *In The Early Days*. Chapter fifteen, titled "An Awful Crime", devoted seven pages to the ghastly brutality of the Cox murder. The author took a cautious lead from Henry Stuart Russell, quoted his denouement, then added: "It is best perhaps to let sleeping dogs lie." Unfortunately for the Maynes, the sleeping dogs barked all over town. The memories of even their most charitable neighbours were awakened. One such near neighbour was John Brenan, the Immigration Officer. He was stationed at "Yungaba", built beside the site of the murder at Kangaroo Point. The Maynes were well aware that everyone knew the unpublished name of the murderer, even if those charitable neighbours kept their silence. There was also Rosanna's continued mental instability, which became part of the gossip about the "mad Maynes". The continued hurt of it all firmed their protective mask of detachment.

Despite their grand outward appearance, perhaps partly because of it, a mantle of new suspicion gradually enveloped them. It was said that all was not right within the walls of "Moorlands". Men came and went, the sounds of parties were heard; the over-protected Mary Emelia, never quite maturing to a stable middle-aged woman and lacking the intelligence of her three clever brothers, was disciplined from time to time. The neighbours kept their distance. Isaac and James had always taken great pride in the gardens at "Moorlands", and despite the new chill in people's attitude, Isaac continued as Vice President of the Horticultural Society of Queensland. The effort to maintain an outwardly normal life could not have been easy. It is possible that at this time, the stress of gossip, isolation and guilt began to disable his finely balanced psyche. There seems to have been a gradual but noticeable change in his behaviour.

Writing of the period, Neil Byrne notes that by the late 1880s the Australian-born Irish Catholics in Brisbane were better placed financially and socially than their immigrant parents. He lists some twenty families in the highest levels of Brisbane society, whose members had achieved their goals in the law, medicine, the civil service and commerce. A.J. Thynne, one of Fr Dunne's pupils, was Minister for Justice; Patrick Real was a puisne judge. In the 1890s education was an important factor in determining exclusiveness, and these men were respected and accepted community leaders.

The three Mayne men, who had as good or better financial and educational advantages, met these families at church and probably did business with many of them, but they remained outsiders. This was despite the fact that, along with many leading professional men of the time whose education had given them a sense of *noblesse oblige*, Dr James Mayne, an acclaimed surgeon at the General Hospital, accepted the responsibility of setting an example by accepting leadership and other offices in several clubs and societies for the public at large. He had entered a caring profession and he cared about every group with which he came in contact. He gave considerable spare time, as well as money for equipment and prizes, to the organisations to which he belonged. In 1895 he was a Member of the Executive of the Queensland National Association. In 1898 he was elected one of the Vice Presidents of the National Cricket Union, and continued as Vice President of the Queensland Cricket Union from 1901 to 1907. From 1898 to 1902 he held the same office with the Brisbane Bicycle Club, and from 1902 to 1903 with the Brisbane Rowing Club.

There were probably many times when James wished himself free of his family and back in the anonymity of London, but his strong sense of responsibility bound him to them. One of his strengths lay in the fact that he had a perceptive and generous understanding of his fellow man. Masking the strain of his private life became a habit. It enabled him to relate more comfortably with his colleagues at the Brisbane General Hospital, where his professional ability was highly regarded. It is on record that the testy Medical Superintendent, Dr E. Sandford Jackson, who demanded efficiency and a high standard, considered him the best assistant at operations that he had ever had. It is also on record that as a resident medical officer, his salary financed the hospital's first X-ray plant. Following his promotion to Medical Superintendent in 1899, he gave all his salary to improvements to the hospital buildings and grounds. Perhaps, like William, he did not waste energy dreaming of the pleasures of a social life relaxing with his contemporaries. The family's basic insecurity, driven by the power of popular gossip, directed the pattern of their life. It was more comfortable to ride with the tide than to resist it.

The tide of gossip ebbed and flowed and strange stories continued to swirl in malevolent currents around them. In honouring the sensible 1865 suggestion that none of them should marry, the Maynes gave substance to the idea that they were all tainted, and this provided a base for the apocryphal murder stories that continued to circulate and protract their stigmatisation. The most frequently heard stories — that are still told — include one in which Patrick murdered an employee and disposed of the body in his mincing machine. No one ever explained how large bones or a head could be crushed in a mid-nineteenth century hand-turned mincer. Another story had one of Patrick's sons arguing with a brother at the butchery and throwing him into a vat of boiling-down fat. This anonymous culprit is said to have taken refuge in the priesthood. The fact that at Patrick's death his three sons were still schoolboys, one as young as four years, was overlooked. And none of them was attracted to a cloistered life.

A Moggill legend, using echoes of the Cox murder, insists that Isaac, a scallywag, held poker and drinking parties on the floating sugar mill *Walrus*, which anchored at riverside sugar farms for the cane to be crushed on board. When a card cheat was discovered, he left the ship and was later found dismembered at the bottom of a well. A supposed inquest concluded that the expert dismembering was done by either a butcher or a doctor, both skills belonging to members of Isaac's supposed party. Again and again these echoes of 1848 are transferred in time and place to prop up an anti-Mayne story. The *Walrus* was small, ninety-six foot long, and somewhat narrow. She had been at times a two-masted schooner and a paddle-wheel steamer, and was refitted in 1869 with a one horse-power engine and a large sugar-crushing machine. There was scant room for the crew, certainly no room for passengers, let alone for them to hold parties. No doubt, once she was anchored at sugar farms along the Brisbane, Logan or Albert rivers, the crew liked to gamble with the locals. The unnamed doctor at the card party could not have been James. *Walrus* was broken up in 1879, while he was still a schoolboy. It is possible that Isaac attended such card games but he was a solicitor, not a butcher, and it would have been a rough, very long horse or carriage ride from

Toowong to Moggill or the downstream farms in order to play a game of cards. No date or year, victim's name, or site of the supposed body's recovery has ever been offered, and no inquest in that period fits the crime. The Moggill legend, like so many other stories, can be considered highly questionable.

Throughout most of those years there was strong Protestant antagonism to the Irish and to Catholics, and most of these stories have an anti-Catholic slant. It is reflected in one of the oldest Mayne stories, that the priest-confessor gave absolution to the murderer, Patrick, on condition that his edict that the children should not marry be obeyed. All these stories are fabrications. Unfortunately, many of the family's fellow-Catholics chose to believe them and withheld friendship. The isolation that stemmed from this found its own outlet. The three sons moved into a life that brought more stress, anxiety, and regrettably, violence. Patrick's sons had none of his cocky self-assertiveness to ride over other people's opinion of them. Their father's abuse of his children, whether mental, moral or physical, had left them with differing coping strategies. With Isaac, it was a time-bomb of pent-up aggression. William, who enjoyed female company, sought sanctuary as a recluse, sheltering from a tempting world. Mary Emelia now seemed content to let the world pass her by. When James strove for a normal life he was to discover the balancing act between self and the world very tricky.

There seems no doubt that for some years Isaac and

British universities, which he had visited. In this pastoral riverside setting, depressing family thoughts and the hurt caused by the carrion feeders of gossip could be laid aside. He could unwind in the peace of the quiet, benign farming area as he strolled with his friend. In a sense it became his refuge from an unsatisfying life. He had always had the ability and drive to be an achiever, but at sixty-four he felt no sense of personal enrichment. All he had was money. He knew that his once promising life was useless, as empty as the vast expanse of clear light that arched above them from Highgate Hill to distant Mt Coot-tha.

In James' mind, St Lucia became *his* place. He could afford to direct its future — give Brisbane its university site. A glance into the distance showed the gently rising slope of the peninsula cradled in the long, curving reaches of the river. It promised the ideal site: acres of flat land for sport and recreation, the river for rowing and swimming, and cleared high land where buildings could rise. With still vivid mental pictures of the 1893 raging floods and the family's relief as their brand-new home stood safe on the rise, he could be confident that this was a unique site where the University could economically maximise the use of all the land and erect buildings above any future threat of flood.

With or without the journalistic efforts of Fred Whitehouse, it was only a few weeks after the *Galmahra* publication that James arrived at his decision. With Mary Emelia's agreement and his agent's assistance, he ascertained the available area at St Lucia and its market price. Then,

James were living what at that time had to be the double life of homosexuals. There was a flourishing homosexual sub-culture in Brisbane, with known points of pick-up at lavatories near the wharf on the south bank, and at the Australian Steam Navigation Company's wharf in Margaret Street. Closer to Isaac's office in Queen Street was the lavatory block used by the staff of hardware merchants Alfred Shaw and Company. That firm had a large staff, including teenagers and young men. Some of them, with other townsmen who frequented the lavatory, came to police notice in 1892.

At that time homosexual acts were regarded as abominable crimes punishable by imprisonment; in medical circles, homosexuality was sometimes considered a form of insanity. Some medical practitioners insisted that homosexuality was an illness which could be cured by electro-convulsive aversion therapy or by castration. The merest suggestion of being involved in such a life meant social suicide. Unspoken knowledge of the Maynes' involvement in such a life was probably a factor in their social non-acceptance. They certainly had little social position to lose, but the opprobrium heaped on any known offender made them exceedingly cautious. Their private life seems to have been conducted at home, where a six-foot closed plank fence was erected inside the white picket boundary fence and kept the identity of visitors from prying eyes. Unfortunately this new secretiveness provided more fuel for the inquisitive and the rumour-mongers. Such people had little to build on, however, and had it not been for a deterioration in Isaac's mental health, the family might eventually have been left in relative peace.

For William, even that kind of illusory peace brought little balm. In January 1897 the Mayne family went on yet another of their holidays to New Zealand — a country where their story was not known, not gossiped about, where they could relax and enjoy a carefree holiday.

William and James both had the classicist's eye for beauty and as the family embarked on a scenic coach tour of both islands, two Australian women joined the group. The younger, Florence Davidson, the travelling companion of a Miss Crompton Roberts, was not only stylish and attractive but an intelligent young woman with a keen sense of fun. She came from Parramatta.

By train, steamer, coach and canoe the travelling party was thrown together. They found extra time for long walks in the evening, singing at the hotel piano, and quiet conversation over supper. Group photographs show clearly that they were a congenial company. By the end of the second week William alone was escorting his sister and Florence Davidson on the evening walks. He bought her sweets, a Christmas book and perfume. He stayed late with her in hotel sitting rooms to play cards or to chat, and as Florence's diary records: "Mr William Mayne and I sat in the back of the coach and we had fun".

On a bone-shaking sixty-five-mile coach trip to Longford, Florence was distressed with travel sickness and William did all he could to make her comfortable. James, the doctor, either saw no need to offer his professional aid or had advised William on how to treat her needs.

At Christchurch, during the last few days of the group's tour Florence's diary notes that William was very kind and generous, and that he spent time alone with her. At Dunedin his four weeks of being attentive to a beautiful young woman came to an abrupt end. The Maynes returned to Australia. Florence, who may have hoped to win the heart of the handsome bachelor, suddenly found her days empty. She complained sadly to her diary: "I feel as if I had lost a shilling and picked up threepence for the next three days. We miss the Maynes. At least I do very much."

In honouring the Mayne family decision that none should marry, the strain on William was probably greater than on Isaac and James who found a different outlet for their sexuality.

Two years later the twenty-four-year-old Florence, no doubt wondering why her hopes for romance had ended so abruptly, set out for Brisbane to renew acquaintance with the Maynes. She was a young lady with good social contacts and with her friend, Kathleen Betts, sailed from Sydney on the steamer *Cintra*. They spent a month with the Boyd family in their home in the grounds of the Immigration Depot next to the imposing "Yungaba", at Kangaroo Point.

Florence had barely unpacked before she prevailed on Mr Boyd to show her over the Brisbane Hospital where Dr James Mayne was Superintendent. Sadly she did not sight him but she was impressed with the new Lady Lamington

Nurses Home for which James Mayne had donated the most comfortable furniture and financed the landscaping of the grounds.

In the busy whirl of Brisbane's winter social season the girls were squired by several eligible young men including Fitz and Cecil Brenan, sons of the Immigration Officer, Mat Cokeley who took them sailing on his yacht, Mr Pring Roberts and others who variously escorted them to receptions at Government House and Bishopbourne polo matches at Ascot, the Masonic Ball and dances. They also attended musical "at homes".

The non-stop entertainment did not deter Florence from her main aim. When she spied William and Mary Emelia in their carriage in town and was not seen by them, she, an Anglican, decided to attend Sunday service at the Roman Catholic cathedral. It was a pleasantly surprised Mary Emelia, not the accompanying William, who invited her to afternoon tea at "Moorlands". Pleased to have a congenial friend visit her, Mary Emelia invited Florence back a week later for luncheon and tennis. William did not appear.

Knowing of the Brisbane family Florence stayed with, virtually on the site of his father's brutal crime, and of the rejection of his family by the establishment families Florence was seeing, William realised that any anonymity the Maynes had in New Zealand was now gone. The sins of the father and all the other hurtful gossip would by now be part of Florence Davidson's enlightenment. He was long practised in withdrawing from an unkind world.

Three days before Florence and her friend returned to Sydney she spent a final afternoon playing tennis at "Moorlands". In the twilight William escorted her across the lawn to Auchenflower station. The diary is eloquently silent on their parting.

At the end of 1898, Dr Sandford Jackson decided to retire as Superintendent of the Brisbane General Hospital. His successor was to be the Resident Medical Officer, Dr James Mayne, now thirty-eight. In view of the family's unhappy background of rumour and innuendo, and the fact that there was another contender for the position, his appointment can only have been on merit. This was testimony to the worth of the real James; the man who might have made his name in the medical field had he not been finally overwhelmed by the actions of Isaac.

The Superintendent's role, with a staff of sixty and more than a dozen honorary medical officers, placed James in a more public position. He was invited to join various committees and held office on them. As he was a bachelor he chose to relinquish the more spacious Superintendent's house to the three resident medical officers, and elected to live in the hospital cottage.

The autocratic Dr Jackson's combination of a private practice with his position as Hospital Superintendent had given rise to a controversial state of affairs which the Hospital Committee was not prepared to condone with any new appointee. In 1899 there was a general tightening of rules; James, living at the hospital, was expected never to absent himself for more than six hours a day. It was a restriction which could have posed difficulties when he was needed at "Moorlands" during some of Isaac's erratic episodes. His transport for the six dusty miles from the hospital was horse-drawn, so any emergency overnight stays at his Toowong home would have been difficult. Over the next four years there were times when a family crisis demanded his time and he was torn between his own professional life and shouldering responsibility for the disquieting behaviour of his family. His record and his colleagues' freely-given praise indicate that he was successfully filling his role.

A photograph taken at this time shows no outward sign of stress. James was a tolerably handsome man with a large head and strong, definite features but was quite dissimilar to his father. His thinning hair was a lighter brown and his firm jawline and calm face, featuring a fashionable guardsman moustache, gave an impression of quiet strength. His nineteenth-century imperialist education had imbued him with the ideals of duty, loyalty, honour and chivalry — but, given the stark reality of the Maynes' family life, his ideals and his professional ambition were to be sorely tested.

By the end of 1902, after only four years in his position as Superintendent, James had to make a decision about Isaac's deteriorating mental health. The whole family would go for a trip to England. It was a cover to seek medical help for his fifty-one year old brother. The decision to seek such help abroad and not in Sydney or Melbourne was partly based on the secrecy the family always employed to screen their troubles from the inquisitive world. They continually sought anonymity. On 8 February 1903, James took six months' leave of absence and Dr McLean stood in as Acting Superintendent. Aunt Ann was left to mind "Moorlands" while Mary Emelia and her three brothers sailed from Sydney on the *India*, bound for London. The passenger list showed 241 people on board and listed Isaac Mayne as a married man with a double cabin. This was either an error, or his condition may have been such that he travelled with a nurse or other attendant.

By July that year it seems they realised that the English doctors could do little to help Isaac. At a time when the family should have been on the high seas heading back to Australia, James cabled the hospital committee to request three months' extension of his leave. Whether this cable came from America or whether they were travelling there is not indicated. The possibility that they sought help in the United States lies in the fact that in later years, Mary Emelia spoke of such a visit. No doubt she and William had an opportunity to enjoy the sights and comb the stores for many of the decorative items that graced their home. They were having nine months' holiday, but for James it was a case of duty to the family and putting his professional ambition on hold. As a medical man he would not have seen Isaac's hereditary problem in isolation. His own homosexuality (still considered a mental disease) would have concerned him. If a search for help in the best medical centres of the world was fruitless, the future for the Mayne brothers looked bleak.

Back at the Brisbane Hospital in mid-November, James had much need of those few understanding colleagues with whom he could relax his guard and discuss the family affliction. There was a professional bond between him and his former superintendent, Dr Jackson, and with the Hospital Dispenser, Douglas Brown, both of whom occasionally visited "Moorlands". He was also able to confide in the tall, mannish Dr Lilian Cooper, Queensland's first woman doctor, who arrived from Britain in 1891 with her female companion Mary Josephine Bedford. Their arrival in the year of James' return from his studies may indicate that they had met in England. As a woman doctor, Lilian Cooper initially had difficulty in finding acceptance, and like James, she kept her private life to herself. The two had much in common and appear to have shared confidences. It was to Lilian Cooper that he confided there were three generations of madness in his family.

The hospital minutes of the period give no explicit indication that anyone knew anything of the Maynes' tragic family history. However, hindsight reveals hints of an invisible component; sometimes the phrasing of sentences suggests that a few members of the committee were well aware of the family background. That this awareness was caring, and provided confidential support for James seems likely. Where it was otherwise, he could only expect a continuation of knowing smiles, nods and winks behind his back.

10
The Tobita Murder and Its Aftermath

IN the crisp morning hours of 9 June 1904, a badly mangled body was found on the railway line a short distance from "Moorlands", between Auchenflower and Milton stations. The victim was Tatsuzo Tobita, twenty-four, a Japanese from Wickham Street in Fortitude Valley. The Maynes had now been home for seven months.

Railway officials and policemen searched along the line collecting pieces of clothing and body which had been widely strewn by a passing train. The searchers and the late Mr Tobita's two fellow Japanese workers were interviewed. At the inquest the facts that emerged were that he was a managing partner of the merchants Asahi and

Company, and had been in Brisbane since December 1902. He was said to be a jolly man, but had behaved erratically the day before he was killed. There was no mention of the Maynes, and since the foreigner had no relations in Australia to query his death his body was buried as a suspected suicide.

Almost immediately a now unmanageable Isaac was confined and restrained at his home at "Moorlands". The window of his room was boarded up and the family were again abruptly faced with the disturbing reality of their inherited prospect of insanity. An anxious James, who best understood the medical possibilities, was expected to be at the General Hospital for eighteen hours of every day. He was a surgeon; that in itself had a frightening connotation. For a responsible man such as he, the uncertainty of all their futures would have amplified the inner chaos and torment he must have been experiencing. Usually, when faced with the strong winds of gossip he was as a blade of grass, now, faced with a brick wall of horror, he was the strong wind. An immediate responsibility was to protect the family from a new threat to the continued aching hurt of their damaged reputation. Another was to help Isaac to any form of mental stability or rehabilitation possible. Nothing could now help the dead Tatsuzo Tobita.

Who restrained Isaac and attended to his needs was never revealed. Perhaps the reclusive William was pressed into service. There were staff at "Moorlands" — a gardener, a carriage driver who attended to the horses and the half-dozen Jersey cows, and a maid. They surely made some connection with the two events. It would have been too much to expect that they would say nothing about the murder at their back door. Nor could the staff at Thomas Bunton's have been entirely ignorant of Isaac's severe personality disorder. If he was still working there, which is unlikely, they would have been given some reason for his absence.

The locals knew it all, of course. The whispers became open discussion, and today's elderly people still recount the handed-down versions of what happened. Their current stories vary widely from the gardener being the victim, to an Italian friend of Isaac's, or a foreign caller who was raped and murdered. Even the then long-deceased John Markwell and his son Henry John Markwell, whose horse threw him in 1868, are sometimes said to be the victims. Strangely, few people today seem to know that the victim was a young Japanese trader who lived and worked several miles from "Moorlands", in Fortitude Valley, and who had taken the train to meet an anonymous person near Toowong. Perhaps Tobita's identity vanished because he was an Asian: in those racist days, no one bothered over-much about a dead Japanese.

In an effort to maintain complete secrecy on this new family scandal they locked their brother away but could not do that forever. If they had hoped that Isaac's condition would improve and he could be quietly kept stable, they hoped in vain. After three months of coping with their uncontrollable brother, to say nothing of enduring the outspoken local comment, James arranged for a month's leave from the Brisbane General Hospital. Again Dr McLean acted as Medical Superintendent.

Isaac was taken to Sydney, a task which would have needed the effort of both brothers, if not a third attendant. The options were to go by train or ship; neither easy with a sedated or restrained patient if any sort of anonymity was to be preserved. To go by train to Sydney meant a change of train at the State border town of Wallangarra. However, this train had the advantage of some privacy. It departed from Central Station and travelled via Ipswich to Wallangarra, so they could quietly board it from their own back gate at Auchenflower station. The names of most Queensland/New South Wales train passengers departing and arriving were listed in the daily press, as were those who came or went by ship. During this period no one named Mayne is listed for either form of transport. The Brisbane Hospital minutes record Dr Mayne as being absent from 4 October 1904 but it was not until 27 October that Isaac was admitted to Bay View Asylum at Cooks River in New South Wales. Once more the care and responsibility for his eldest brother, and loyalty to the family, were forcing James to neglect his own professional ambition and any hope for some sort of normalcy in his life.

Two days before Isaac was admitted to Bay View, at a Brisbane General Hospital meeting, Dr Hertzberg reported that Dr James Mayne was suffering a painful illness with a poisoned hand in the Sydney Hospital and that he was pleased to hear that he was recovering. A month's extension of leave was granted to Dr Mayne.

In fact James does not appear to have been in hospital at all, but arranging more permanent psychiatric care of Isaac; who, quite probably, was the one in a Sydney hospital. It seems more likely that the recorded minute indicates the way James' colleagues in Brisbane understood his difficulty and respected his wish for privacy. If so, they were affording him the only help and support they could. The evidence provides a strong possibility that, accepting his own sexuality and fearing its effect on his sanity, especially in the light of Isaac's mid-life breakdown, James did ultimately admit himself to Sydney Hospital for tests and treatment. If so, that would have occurred between 28 October and 26 November 1904, after Isaac was admitted to Bay View. This cannot be proved or disproved: those Sydney Hospital records were destroyed some fifty years ago.

For James it now seemed to be a matter of maintaining as much secrecy as he could and covering for Isaac's actions at all costs. The ultimate cost was the truth and the wreck of the rest of James' professional life. Isaac was admitted to Bay View in a state of acute melancholia. James, who committed him, told the two examining doctors that Isaac had business worries, there were no insane relations, and his habits were normally active but gentle and temperate. He added that this had been Isaac's only attack, and that it had occurred only two months earlier. Every one of those statements was incorrect. They were surprising, coming from a medically trained brother whose genuine aim was to secure Isaac's recovery or improvement. A strategic inked-in question mark at the end of James' recorded information at Bay View suggests that the admitting doctors did not entirely believe him.

It seems that a lifetime of covering one's background against spiteful schoolboys, curious neighbours and inquisitive colleagues, made James' adoption of a shadowy, evasive life almost second nature. To survive as well as they did, the Maynes may have needed to habitually dissemble.

At Bay View the admitting doctors noted that Isaac was stout and very nervous. "… continually anxious and suspicious as though expecting something to happen of a dreadful character. He was sleepless and full of melancholic delusions". James did admit that his brother had been restrained and under constant supervision to guard against self-injury, but he gave an incorrect duration of that confinement at "Moorlands" — two months instead of three. His fear could have been that to tell the exact truth might have ultimately incriminated Isaac in any future examination of Tatsuzo Tobita's death.

It was now, if at all, that James sought medical help for himself. If nothing else, the last five months must have exhausted him mentally and physically. He was known to be a very humane and gentle man, but he carried the guilt for all the family in covering up for Isaac. The lies he had to tell, apprehension that the deception might all come undone, the constant fear that William, Mary Emelia, or he himself would sooner or later have to walk down that same dread path as their father, sister, and brother, must have been an unrelenting torment. And for James, as a surgeon, there was that added dread of a breakdown at the Brisbane General Hospital.

He arrived back at Brisbane on the night of 28 November, and the following morning called on James Stodart, MLA, the Chairman of the hospital Committee of Management, and offered to resign. The reason given was a personal health problem. Stodart assured him that the Committee would grant him an extension of leave until he felt able to cope with his hospital responsibilities. James was adamant that he would resign. It was, no doubt, some balm to his shattered spirit that his ability as a doctor and administrator was valued, but he knew that if the truth ever emerged, his carefully built-up world would disintegrate. He would not have that disgrace reflected on the Brisbane General Hospital. Despite Stodart's urging that he reconsider, the next day James wrote to the Chairman:

> In pursuance of my interview with you yesterday I beg you to be so good as to place my resignation in the hands of the Committee with the request that they will do me the favour to permit my *locum tenens* to continue to act on my behalf until they have completed arrangements for my succession.
>
> As you are aware my health had been unsatisfactory for some time and the distress that I have lately undergone has left me quite unfit to take up work again. If I were not assured that I must be free from such responsibility for some considerable time I would not have adopted this course

which is determined upon after mature deliberation and at the cost of personal inclination.

1 December 1904.

He also resigned from all clubs and associations except the Queensland Cricket Association. A less sensitive, less caring man would have ridden out the storm, been open about his brother's illness, and kept on with his profession. James was not built that way. If proof was needed that within the hospital hierarchy James' and Isaac's story was wide-open and discussed, one only needs to see the three exclamation marks which the secretary has irreverently entered in the column beside the minute noting James' excuse for his resignation.

Nothing James did could take the heat of gossip from the family. All the covering-up did no more than cloud the truth and promote speculation. When the *Brisbane Courier* noted his resignation as Hospital Superintendent on 3 December 1904, it gave the reason as "ill health". Some mentioned the damaged hand. Across town that did little but raise eyebrows. As the senior brother, William's role in the decision-making about Isaac could not have been non-existent, but by keeping an extremely low profile, he did not exist for the newspapers or gossipmongers. In fact not many people knew that there was a brother called William.

It was now December. The festive season was under way. For the Mayne household it would have been an understatement to say that Christmas 1904 was bleak.

Almost immediately another tragedy enveloped the Maynes in gossip. This was the death of the twenty-one-year-old Carl Markwell, on 24 January 1905. In the vast amount of evidence taken at this inquest not one published word links him to the Maynes. Unfortunately, their story has been so overlaid with fantasy that it was predictable the family would be linked to the bizarre death of a young homosexual whose friends included rich men about town. Occurring so soon after Tatsuzo Tobita's death and the public belief that Isaac Mayne had killed him, any good mystery would have been attributed to them.

The name Markwell as a victim is constantly and erroneously linked to Isaac. Quite possibly this arose because, over time, public gossip, now linking Carl Markwell and Isaac as the murderers of Tatsuzo Tobita, became confused with the name of Mayne's former neighbour, a different but related family of Markwells who had sold "Moorlands Villa" to the Maynes. The tragic history of that family has already been mentioned, but as today's persistent myth includes both Markwell families, some clarification is necessary. It is well documented that the fatal riding accident of young Henry John Markwell took place on River Road, Toowong, in 1868. The people who witnessed the accident carried him to his father's house, "Moorlands Villa", where he died. At that time, Patrick Mayne was dead, and Isaac was a schoolboy living with his family next to the butchery in Queen Street. In 1881, John Markwell senior died of natural causes at "Moorlands Villa". A current popular story which also needs to be debunked is that Georgina, supposedly Patrick Mayne's first wife, haunts "Moorlands". Patrick's only wife was Mary. Georgina was John Markwell's second wife. After she died in childbirth, John married again. The widow he left was Harriet. If any of Markwell's wives wanted to do any haunting, one would suppose they would do it on the site of "Moorlands Villa", further up the hill, where Wesley Hospital now stands.

As the Carl Markwell death in 1905 was, and still is, so persistently linked to Isaac Mayne, its coincidental evidence and timing must be examined. Two days after James returned from Sydney, young Markwell, an office clerk, began insuring himself with five companies for a total of £2,250 and made a somewhat unusual will. Two well-known Brisbane men were his trustees and his bequests to his mother and two sisters were on condition that they did not commit adultery before marriage. Until a few weeks before his death, Markwell's wages as a clerk with the merchants, Siemons, in Roma Street had been twenty-five shillings a week, but with a change of job, he earned thirty shillings and paid twenty of them to his mother for board. Despite the fact that he had no other money except the balance of his wages, he owned a collection of several pieces of gold and silver jewellery and some valuable gem-studded tie pins. A photograph of one of his trustees, wearing a velvet trimmed jacket and a silk top hat was among his effects. He had frequently spoken of going for a trip to New Zealand, a favourite holiday destination of the Maynes, and he had discovered enough about the symptoms of epilepsy to fake them and convince a doctor that he was an epileptic.

In the early evening of 24 January 1905, he and his sister had taken a long tram ride from his home in the eastern suburb of Wooloowin to the western suburb of Toowong and then home again. He then stepped into a hot bath and drank potassium cyanide. The faked epilepsy was to suggest accidental drowning so that the insurance could be claimed.

Taking tram rides was a common pastime in those days, but the fact that Carl Markwell went to Toowong gave rise to gossip that he went to the Maynes. The tram route was two blocks distant from "Moorlands". It was the train which had a station at their back gate, but walking was also a common pastime and there may not have been a scheduled train at a suitable time. Selina Joyce, a housemaid from Toowong, gave evidence. Neither her employer's name nor address was stated, but she proved to be a family friend of the young Markwells. Speculation was stirred when the question arose as to how and where Carl had obtained cyanide and detailed knowledge of the symptoms of epilepsy. Clutching at any link, the rumourmongers noted that a friend of James who visited "Moorlands" was the Hospital Dispenser, Douglas Brown. A magisterial inquiry was held and the body, immediately exhumed, was found to contain traces of potassium cyanide, commonly used by photographers, and not hydrogen cyanide. The photography shop and the salesman were easily identified. There was no link with James Mayne or his friend.

The wild speculation surrounding Carl Markwell's death is tangled and full of half-truths. No reason was offered for his suicide; simplification would be falsification. There was time between James' return from Sydney and Markwell's detailed insurance and suicide plans for him to have learned from James that Isaac had been declared insane and committed to an asylum. Other members of the household could have told him earlier, but that is drawing a long bow and suggesting that Isaac and Carl were friends. Nothing in the evidence suggests that they knew each other. I contend that it was quite coincidental that within a week of Carl Markwell's suicide, Isaac Mayne hanged himself.

Brisbane's court of public opinion decided that Isaac and Carl were involved in a lovers' pact. The facts are that the Mayne family had been excessively secret about Isaac's committal to Bay View. Few, if any, outside of the family knew, and it is highly unlikely that they told a young caller who may, or may not, have known Isaac. That is, unless the housemaid who gave evidence worked at "Moorlands". Had Markwell been at "Moorlands" on the night of Tobita's death and been associated with Isaac in that crime, it is even more unlikely that the family would impart to him knowledge of their brother's whereabouts. The gossiping public only learned where he was when, on 1 February 1905, the *Sydney Morning Herald* headed an item "SUICIDE IN AN ASYLUM" and noted that "in a private asylum for the insane at Cooks River ... Isaac Mayne, a solicitor ... a native of Queensland ..." The local papers took up the item. As for Isaac learning of a supposed friend's death before taking his own life, that, too, is most unlikely. He had been under supervision and restraint for his own safety at both "Moorlands" and Bay View Asylum. To take his own life he had to exercise the same sort of cunning as was evident in some of his father's actions. He acted on a chance opportunity. When his attendant left his room briefly at 5 a.m. on 31 January, Isaac, who was thought to be asleep, disappeared. He was found two hours later suspended from a beam in the asylum pottery shed. He was fifty-three.

James, so vulnerable, was acutely sensitive to the new vicious and unsubstantiated gossip. With a need to put the whole miserable story behind them forever, he fanned the gossip by acting with more haste than commonsense. Isaac's body was railed to Brisbane on the day of his death, and, because of the heat of midsummer, buried at Toowong within hours of arrival. — Suspicious haste, murmured Dame Rumour. But no secret was made of the funeral; notices appeared in the Brisbane press. The public wanted to suspect a cover-up and misread James' reason for haste.

Isaac had made no will and Rosanna and Mary Emelia consented to letters of administration being granted to William and James to settle his affairs. Almost all of his estate was held in some fifty parcels of land sited in the

City, North Brisbane, Kedron, Enoggera, Yeerongpilly and Sandgate. They were valued at £21,379 and the decision was to consolidate, rather than fragment the family's wealth. Following their mother's lead, it was considered that Rosanna's dowry, consisting of her inheritance from Patrick's estate, needed no enlarging. On 19 April 1905, in a deed of assignment, Rosanna agreed with that decision and assigned her title to the others. Her steady signature on her receipt for a token payment of ten shillings cleared the way for the other three to inherit. On these documents a glimpse of the elusive William peeps through the legalities. Everywhere he is listed as "William Mayne, Gentleman". Perhaps his gentlemanly hand is also reflected on Isaac's death certificate. On earlier documents, their father was always recorded as a butcher, but in 1905 he is promoted to "Patrick Mayne, Grazier". In cases where the information seems to come from James, he, a little more accurately, recorded his father as "butcher and grazier".

The three youngest Maynes had been under very severe tension for more than three years, long before they went overseas to seek help for Isaac. Rosanna's condition, now needing more frequent periods of restraint, had been a worry almost as long as Mary Emelia and James could remember. But she was receiving the recommended care of the day in the security of All Hallows', and was not disrupting their daily lives as Isaac had. They had all been born to tension and had lived with it for much of their life, but none of it had wreaked the havoc created by Isaac in the last few years. How they fared psychologically is unknown, but four months after Isaac's suicide, Ann Mayne, seventy-six, died at "Moorlands". Now the emptiness of being idle, monied, and shunned, descended on the three surviving members of the family.

11

The Burden of Inheritance

BETWEEN 1905 and 1918 the only known activities of the surviving Maynes were the maintenance and increasing of their large property holdings, William's horse riding, and long carriage trips to their land at Moggill for leisurely picnics. The land was leased to James Pacey, a farming son of the Irish ticket-of-leave Patrick Pacey who had befriended Patrick Mayne when the slaughterhouse moved to that area in 1848. Although the farmers knew of Patrick's crime, the murder at Milton and the legend of Isaac on the *Walrus*, many had a high regard for the three youngest Maynes. The middle-aged James and Mary Emelia are remembered as gentle, kindly people who brought little gifts and sweets for the local children.

Folk in the neighbourhood between Milton and

Toowong remember them very differently. During the first decade of the new century many of the gardens of those early large houses were sliced into profitable smaller allotments, and the spaces rapidly filled by less wealthy but still comfortably-off families in smaller houses. The new arrivals were quickly aware of the mysterious, wealthy Maynes. They heard all the garbled murder stories and feared the unspeakable rumours. Their children, searching for after-school adventure beneath the twisted green canopy of Langsville Creek and the marshy reeds, were forbidden to go beyond that area onto the Maynes' land. Those children, today's octogenarians, were never told what their parents feared, only that the place was "evil" or a "bad place". The word *homosexual* was not in use until the 1890s. It was still not generally spoken; as late as 1917, the "crime" of homosexuality could attract a gaol sentence of fourteen years — more commonly, a harsh seven years. The community was very concerned with respectability. Most people feared public shame. A strict morality cemented the public ethos.

It was quite customary for many of the children of apprehensive parents to obediently avert their eyes as they hurried past the big house on River Road on their way to or from school. No doubt with shivers of mysterious excitation. In the 1920s my husband, then a wandering, adventurous child, swam in the creek that separated his home, "Ravensfield" from "Moorlands". With his equally adventurous friends, he combed the marshy banks for snakes and birds' nests, but they dared go no closer to "that place". To them, one window, boarded up ever since Isaac's incarceration, was a grim signal of the unspeakable events rumoured to take place there. Were they still happening or did they belong to the past? No one knew. No one tested the rumours that hung in a black miasma over "Moorlands", piquing the ever-curious minds that hid behind many restrained, down-drawn, condemning lips. Even across the river, from Davies Park to Hill End, the locals would aim one thumb in the direction of "Moorlands" and tell all who would listen of the evil that lurked there.

Such long-term mass condemnation of a family is a subject for others to study. The two sinners were dead. Those who lived on were quiet, well-mannered, churchgoing and public spirited. They harmed no one. The only accusation that could be levelled at was one of homosexuality, and that word was never uttered. Its non-mention has allowed it to disappear from almost all the Mayne stories, leaving "All those murders!" to be the general reaction when one inquires about the Maynes.

There were friends, but not many. Archbishop Dunne, who valued social harmony above strict religious teaching, was still alive, though feeble. He was not a man to judge those who walked along different paths and his friendship and guidance over the years had always been warm. He had been more interested in building schools than churches, and had never approved the bricks-and-mortar Catholicism of his predecessor, James Quinn. Neither did he approve of building programmes which ran into debt.

His was a philosophy which appealed to William and James. One thing they had learned or inherited from their parents was good business sense. They husbanded their wealth and probably William, certainly James, gave a lot of thought to how it could be best used. Archbishop Dunne's influence on the Mayne family seems to have been much stronger than has been realised. This became apparent under the reign of his successor. The very different, big-spending James Duhig, who in 1912 became co-adjutor Archbishop and in 1917 received the pallium, had a philosophy which did not appeal to James. The two never became friends.

With the outbreak of war in 1914, James and William were too old to enlist as soldiers. But one of the questions which must arise is why the patriotic James Mayne, who daily flew the Union Jack above "Moorlands", did not offer his medical skills to the forces. He had remained a registered medical practitioner, and at fifty-three his age was no barrier. In 1914 the slightly older Ernest Sandford Jackson abandoned his private practice and quickly donned the uniform of a major serving with the 1st Australian General Hospital. Doctors were in short supply and James would be well aware of the need, particularly for surgeons in the field. Was it a burning dread, anticipation even of the insanity that dogged the family, especially its two knife-wielding members? Perhaps he did offer, only to be turned down. It is not easy to reconcile the patriotic man of strong character with the determination to spend years in serious study towards his goal, with the man who now idled away his life when surgeons were urgently needed.

It has been said that Mary Emelia's war effort involved a sewing circle at their home. The Red Cross Annual Reports reveal that an army of volunteer women spent their spare time in the industrious making of pyjamas, pillow-slips, fly veils, balaclavas and socks, and the turning of a myriad pieces of material into hospital needs. In most cases groups were led by the wives of local establishment men: bankers, lawyers, doctors or politicians. At Toowong, the Red Cross and the Boy Scouts each had a ladies' committee and there was a Girls' Patriotic Fund. A Toowong/Auchenflower branch of the Red Cross was led by Lady Philp in her home. There is no mention of the name Mayne, nor of "Moorlands" as a working-bee venue among the very long list in the records. If Mary Emelia did put her home and money at the disposal of a volunteer sewing circle, it must have comprised a handful of local women whom she knew. Like countless other women contributors to the war effort, she does not appear to have worked in any organised manner.

Just before the war a group of young men had reformed the Toowong Rowing Club, which had lapsed after losing its shed and equipment in the 1893 flood. In 1918 James became its President, an office he held for several years. At the age of fifty-nine it was through rowing that he met twenty-year-old university student, Frederick White-house. A close relationship developed between them which lasted until James died; for Fred, loyalty to James stretched beyond the grave. With his young friend, James rediscovered something of his youth. In his own student days in Sydney and London the heroes were the good athletes with a sense of leadership, courage, and the virtue that lay in winning. Whitehouse, a short, stocky, personable but rather ordinary-looking student, had many admirable qualities. An active oarsman, he was as enthusiastic a sport as he was a science student, and took a lead in student and community affairs. He is remembered as a self-contained, tough little man. His flair for debating and journalism was a spark to quicken James' own sharp intelligence.

The bright, enthusiastic young Whitehouse would have brought a ray of sunshine to the colourless existence in post-war "Moorlands". William, now in his mid-sixties, had been slowed by heart disease. The once hyperactive, flighty Mary Emelia, now dull and compliant, rigidly buttoned into sombre pre-war long dresses and black buttoned-up boots, had little enthusiasm for anything other than going to church, domestic responsibilities, and picnics at Moggill. It was the flapper era; short skirts, the Charleston and jazz music, but such changes had not pervaded "Moorlands".

There was little to draw visitors had they wished to come. A few old friends such as Dr Sandford Jackson called, so did their estate agent, and the new Archbishop, James Duhig. Jackson had been the family doctor since the turn of the century. His were both professional and friendly visits. With William he shared a knowledge and love of good horses. With James, there were medical issues to discuss, and with both brothers the shared joy of creating beautiful gardens, and that long-running contentious topic, the potential of three sites proposed for the expansion of the University. Jackson and many others in the medical profession were adamant that it should be sited at Victoria Park, near the General Hospital. James and his new young friend Fred Whitehouse argued for space for buildings and playing fields and a rowing shed by the river. They were more in tune with some public arguments which ranged around the merits of the other sites — Dutton Park at Yeronga, and St Lucia. The government had little money for expansion and so the argument rolled on across the years.

After William's death on 16 August 1921, there were longer intervals between visitors to "Moorlands". Within a few months Fred graduated and won a travelling scholarship to Cambridge University. He and James used to stroll along the river bank at Toowong, talking and debating a wide variety of issues. Despite their age disparity, for James this was one of the better periods of his life. Now that, too, came to an end. The long days with only Mary Emelia for company were tedious. He sought more outside interests. There was some involvement with the Amateur Fishermen's Association. His generosity paid for extensive improvements to its Douglas Ogilvy cottage at Bribie Island, and in the 1930s, he gave money to build a Stradbroke Island cottage near the headland at Point Lookout. They elected him Vice President of their association and named the new building "James Mayne Cottage". It is difficult to imagine the fastidious James as a fisherman, spending weekends in the small, spartan weekender. By the 1980s his name on the cottage had been supplanted by a sign reading "Tug Tellum" — the reverse of mullet gut. James Mayne had been forgotten. The cottage withstood the onslaught of storms and tourists, but in 1995 it was removed by developers in the name of progress.

When William died, Rosanna was again excluded from inheriting. Mary Emelia and James were his beneficiaries and executors. Mary Emelia was to receive the special bequest of £5,000 which William thought she had been denied in her mother's will; the remainder of his £54,000 estate was divided equally between the two. Almost all of it was real property and inscribed stock. As Mary Emelia had never been interested in business matters and was quite content to follow James' lead, the real responsibility for their joint wealth now fell to James. These two, both in their sixties, were among the richest people in the State. They had no descendants. Archbishop Duhig assumed that the Church would eventually inherit. "Moorlands" was high on his visiting list.

In 1922 when St Stephen's Cathedral was being extended eastwards from the nave, Duhig was encouraged when the two Maynes agreed to enhance the high sanctuary wall behind the altar with a large stained-glass window in memory of Isaac and William. As the Archbishop was about to make an overseas trip they gave him a free hand to choose and purchase this memorial. Duhig sought out Dublin's Harry Clarke, one of this century's major designers of stained-glass. He drew his inspiration from the vivid colours of the great Gothic windows of the Middle Ages, and produced a brilliant, translucent mosaic, delicately detailed and dramatic in composition. A triptych that soars almost to the roof, its central panel depicts Christ on a sea of jewelled clouds ascending into heaven while below him is a thoughtful Virgin Mary. Looking on from the side panels are eleven apostles — no Judas. Duhig had chosen well. When the window was unveiled and dedicated by Monseigneur Cattaneo on 10 June 1923 and the bright sun streamed through the splendour of its Byzantine colours, it was evident that the memorial to the two eldest Mayne brothers was a priceless asset for the Cathedral and for Brisbane.

There were now three stained-glass memorial windows to the family in the Cathedral. It is popularly believed by many in the Catholic hierarchy that James now said, "This is the last thing the Church is getting from me". It was in fact the last gift, but the Archbishop, often hard-pressed for money, continued to hope and make requests to him for funds. Duhig misread or refused to see the signals. James was a charming, cordial retiring man, a regular church-goer, but he was also strong-minded. Under the most extreme circumstances he had not hesitated to be decisive and firm in his purpose. That purpose had always been based on what was best for the family; his efforts were always aimed at restoring dignity to their name within the wider community. James' education had not been exclusively Catholic; it had not reinforced his religion. There was little or no sectarian inclusiveness in his make-up. In 1919 he had donated handsomely to the Anglican fund for the new St Martin's War Memorial Hospital. He did not like to be asked for money. He enjoyed the pleasure of spontaneous giving. It was his next big donation that should have sent a message to his Archbishop.

In March 1923, J.D. Story, a Government appointee to the University Senate, suggested that a State which depended on primary industry should offer higher education in that discipline, and the Senate resolved to create a Faculty of Agriculture. It was to operate from 1926. The idea interested James Mayne. His long-running debates with Sandford Jackson about the best site for a university had never abated, but both men were well aware that there was never sufficient money and that good proposals had foundered for lack of it. James' horizon was wider than Jackson's. His vision was for Australia; and it was not centred solely on the needs of the medical profession from which he had withdrawn almost twenty years earlier. He believed that Story's idea should not fail for lack of money or be quietly dropped between then and the proposed operative date of 1926.

The Maynes owned 693 acres of farmland at the junction of Moggill Creek and the Brisbane River. Ever generous where he saw a positive community need, James offered it to the young University to facilitate the founding of the proposed Faculty of Agriculture. The University Senate expressed delight and accepted the gift but was not sure what to do with it. Patrick Mayne had grazed cattle there and the family's lessees still farmed it, but now, under University ownership, trees were cleared and the soil declared unsuitable for agricultural development and grazing. What the Maynes thought of this is unrecorded; they were probably never told. Time quietly erased public knowledge of their gift. The property was again leased out to farmers, and in 1935, during the Depression, it was made available to the State Department of Agriculture and Stock, which moved its Farm School from the St Lucia district to the University's Moggill land. It was some thirty years before the Maynes' gift of that land was put to use by the University in the way its donors had intended. By then, James and Mary Emelia were long dead, but during their lifetimes they continued to have faith in the usefulness of their donation to help education and the nation's primary industry. That was demonstrated in 1940 when it became known that as part of their final munificent bequest, they had willed "Moorlands" to the University. It had once been their hope that it could be used as the administrative heart of the Faculty of Agriculture.

1922 and 1923 were years of big financial decisions. Having donated handsomely to St Stephen's Cathedral, St Martin's Hospital, and the young University of Queensland, James decided to restructure some of the family investments. He would demolish their central city buildings — back-to-back, they stretched from Queen to Adelaide Streets — and erect in their place a three-storied traditional European shopping arcade. As far-seeing a business man as his father, he employed Richard Gailey Jnr, the son of his former architect to design the Brisbane Arcade, which would house a large number of small specialty shops, a restaurant and a top floor of offices, all returning rents on his £70,000 investment. When the Arcade opened at the end of 1923 its Edwardian baroque-style facades and lofty clerestory lighting were much admired. It became a most popular shopping venue. Few, if any of the ladies trying on the latest fashions or lunching with friends in the restaurant realised that on that site sixty years earlier, Mary Mayne had borne her youngest children, the dying Patrick had confessed to a murder, and his resourceful widow had plied the butchery trade to preserve the inheritance which finally financed this modern arcade.

As the decade slipped by James was occasionally reminded that sixty years of family stress had taken their toll. He began facing the one great certainty of life. Of his two older sisters, Rosanna, now in her mid-seventies, existed in a turbulent mental state. She required constant restraint and imposed heavy demands on the concerned Sisters of Mercy. Mary Emelia, in her mid-sixties, was not endowed with the ability to handle business affairs, nor motivated to try. It is likely that her genetic inheritance was a lower than average intelligence and that time or medication had left her dull and listless. Both sisters could outlive him. Neither was capable of dealing with their wealth. Despite their recent largess, he and Mary Emelia were still the possessors of an ever-growing fortune. For a man as responsible as James, its ultimate disposition was a matter of great concern.

12

Maynes and the University of Queensland

BY 1922, the University at George Street was so short of space it was bursting at its dilapidated seams. Some buildings had not been painted since 1910, and white-ant infestation rendered others decidedly hazardous. In September, Parliament had confirmed that 170 acres at Victoria Park, close to the Brisbane Hospital, had now been vested in the University. But the joy of the proponents of that site was shortlived. Their dreams of noble buildings were grievously dashed with the 1925 announcement of the cost of levelling the site before any building could begin. It was estimated at a then astronomical £89,000, which soon soared to £130,000. It was clear to many —

and the press was adamant — that to proceed at Victoria Park would be a costly mistake. The disappointment, and the urgent need to move the University from George Street put heat and vigour into the reopened debate about where the University should be built. The other two optional sites came back into contention: 122 acres at Yeronga or 274 acres at St Lucia.

In October of that year, when the debate was at its height, the geologist Fred Whitehouse returned from Cambridge with a Ph.D., joined the staff at the University, and, in his continued friendship with James, resumed long riverside walks. It is most likely that the clamour of the debate had set James mulling over ideas for a new bequest. Forty-four years later, when Dr Whitehouse was protesting to the University about lack of recognition for James Mayne, he said that in their discussions James was firmly against Victoria Park because it was not possible to row there. Whitehouse wrote: "He and I discussed what river sites were available. He was greatly taken with the nearest of those, the river pocket at St Lucia."

It is tempting to see the persuasive hand of Fred in the next moves that influenced James. They were close friends and Fred was also deeply interested in the future of his University. He was a very able organiser and an active writer who knew the power of the printed word. On 7 January 1926, the *Daily Mail* devoted a leading article to the needs of the young, makeshift University at George Street. The urgency was not just for the Government to provide adequate buildings, but for endowments by wealthy citizens to facilitate the establishment of additional faculties.

Fred would have known much of James' thinking; most likely he decided it was time to give a push to those ideas by urging Eric Tommerup, the editor of the student magazine *Galmahra* to publish what they hoped would prove a catalyst. The May issue of *Galmahra*, to which Fred was a contributor and which he was to edit the following year, aptly headed an item "A Futurist Ramble". Referring to the *Daily Mail* article, it read: "Those lines might appeal to some aged and unmarried plutocrat who is anxious to dispose of his worldly goods in preparation for a life where finance makes less stringent demands ... The University needs a permanent home ... the need is great. It matters not whether the funds are made available from public or private sources but without them, the University cannot play its proper part in the development of Queensland."

This was followed in July by the news that the University Senate had formally created a Chair of Agriculture and that the Faculty was under consideration. It was more than three years since the Maynes had gifted their Moggill land; although nothing much was being done with it, at last the Maynes could enjoy the satisfying thought that their gift was a factor in the Senate decision.

The long walks to rural St Lucia were a time for contemplation. James' memories of undergraduate days at the University of Sydney were of lack of space and no quiet river banks where students could stroll while arguing the problems that exercised their minds, as they did at the

bowler-hatted and with a bright flower in his buttonhole, he called at the City Hall and asked to see the Mayor, William Jolly.

The two had never met. When James began to talk about St Lucia and the urgency of a permanent university site, Jolly cautiously remarked, "But that will cost a lot of money".

To his astonishment, James answered, "Even if it costs £100,000 my sister and I wish to make the gift." That discussion, in early September 1926, was private. Jolly was invited to "Moorlands" for further discussions. It was assumed that the cost of resuming the land would be some £50,000. The question arose: "What if the University declines your offer?" There was no vacillation in James' intention to benefit the community. "The people of Brisbane could have it as a public park," he replied.

By 16 October, to Jolly's dismay, the University Senate released to the press his private advice to them that an anonymous donor had offered to purchase the St Lucia land so that Queensland could have a permanent home for its University. Two weeks later, with nothing decided, the name of Mayne was divulged. James and Mary Emelia featured in a welter of positive publicity; but if they imagined that a grateful University Senate would say "thank you" and welcome this second magnificent gift, they were to be disappointed.

One group, powerful in the academic and medical world and unable to visualise a viable university more than a stone's throw from its teaching hospital, threw up several spurious arguments as to why St Lucia was unsuitable. It was too far out in the bush. Students would not travel the distance. The river mists were unhealthy; students could die of asthma or pneumonia.

The Lord Mayor, having now formed a genuine friendship with James, mounted a pro-St Lucia argument, saying, "This is a site unequalled for a university in any city in Australia or in the world." The Student's Union, fed up with deplorable conditions and the selfishness of the medical group, and casting a hungry eye on the space for sporting facilities, backed the Mayor's opinion. In what must have been music to James' ears, the Union President, Colin Nash, pointed out that via West End, St Lucia was only 1¼ miles from Victoria Bridge and far more suitable than Victoria Park, with its noisy rail traffic. Nash asked whether it was a good policy to seriously endanger the ultimate development of all other faculties by granting an advantage to the Faculty of Medicine.

In mid-December James was invited to meet the Senate to present his views. The result? Subject to a variety of conditions and by the narrowest margin of one vote, it was agreed to accept the land. The ultimate cost was £80,000, well up on the original estimate of £50,000, but as Alderman Jolly recalled, "That was all right, Dr Mayne paid the balance as if he had been expecting to do so".

A very pleased Fred Whitehouse, now editor of *Galmahra*, wrote glowingly of the site and praised "the wise move and the generosity of Dr Mayne, one of the University's best friends". The *Queenslander* managed to get a short interview with Mary Emelia in which she hoped that the health-giving breezes of St Lucia would benefit the students. "Cooking," she said, "is the most important of all branches of knowledge for a woman" — she would like to see it as a subject for a university career. No photograph was taken; without comment, the article was illustrated with one taken when she was nineteen and quite good-looking.

The publicity died away. Everything remained very tenuous. Negotiations, sometimes quite acrimonious, between the Brisbane City Council and the University Senate dragged on. Over the next few years the Senate minutes are studded with the on-and-off arguments about the St Lucia site. The City Council declined to hand over the Mayne gift until the Senate gave a firm declaration that the new University would be built there and the 170 acres at Victoria Park handed back to the Council. This assurance was not given until 1930. On 16 May 1930, the press recorded the public handing-over with James and the Mayor shaking hands. It is an indication of the indecision that continued to reign that four years later, the *Courier Mail* (23 July 1934) noted that the University was twenty-five years old and said: "If the government should decide upon St Lucia as a future site ..."

It is to be wondered if (then as now) the University in fact wanted the valuable gift, but would have preferred the donors to have been other than the Maynes. Doubtless James hoped that as the University grew and became a principal institution within the State, the endowment would restore some long-term merit to his family name. Unfortunately, the University Senate was (and continued to be) singularly insensitive in the matter of honouring the Maynes. Malcolm Thomis, in *A Place of Light & Learning* wrote: "It was a pity that Dr Mayne's magnificent generosity, a munificence universally applauded, should have been followed by this wrangle. It was a pity, too, that this man should have been required to wait almost four years before the gift was finally received. The whole process must have been less than encouraging to other prospective donors in the community."

It was more than four years before the gift site saw any building. Plans were drawn and redrawn and the arguments rolled on. Eleven years after the gift offer was made to Alderman Jolly, the foundation stone was laid on 6 March 1937. Sadly, for the Maynes, the 693 acres of Moggill land, which they had given in 1923 to facilitate the Faculty of Agriculture, was also still awaiting use by the University. It says something for the commitment of James that he and his sister did not waver from their intention of benefiting the community by assisting the University. This also says something about the quality of James' friendship. Dr Sandford Jackson, who was President of the Queensland branch of the British Medical Association, was one of the fiercest opponents of the St Lucia site during the long years of the great debate, yet he and James remained life-long friends.

In 1926 the disclosure of the Maynes' offer had come as something of a shock to Archbishop Duhig. However, he was one of the university senators who favoured building on the St Lucia site and publicly approved the Maynes' generosity. He also stepped up his visits to "Moorlands". On one occasion, when the Mayor was visiting with his young son, Norman, the Archbishop was seen coming up the driveway. Jolly gathered up his son, saying, "We'll go now, Dr Mayne" — but James responded: "Oh Jolly, don't leave me with that awful man."

James' dislike of his Archbishop was long-standing and ongoing, but Duhig continued to visit. In July 1927 the Archbishop wrote to James and a group of thirty-eight wealthy Catholics requesting generous financial help for his new project, the Holy Name Cathedral. It was to be built on the commanding site of "Dara", once owned by Patrick Mayne and since 1891 the charming, three-storied Italianate home of the archbishops. Like Archbishop Dunne, James believed it was more important to provide good education for young Catholics than to erect prestigious buildings. He could not approve the waste of knocking down such a gracious building to put another in its place, especially with the threat of economic depression sapping business confidence. He thought that St Stephen's Cathedral with its magnificent stained-glass windows was quite adequate. The Archbishop's letter attracted a good response, and those civic leaders who gave most generously received Papal knighthoods in 1929. The Maynes, who gave nothing, went unhonoured.

It is hard to know whether James' lack of response to the financially embarrassed Archbishop and his building appeal made Duhig give vent to anger against him, or whether Rosanna, now almost eighty and very ill at All Hallows', had become too much of a burden on the sisters and they wanted her moved. Undoubtedly her mental instability had loaded an extra cross on her carers. Late in 1929, Duhig wrote to James indicating that it was time he took over the care of his sister.

Neither the elderly James nor Mary Emelia was able to nurse a woman with advanced senile decay, kept under physical restraint. It would be a matter of shifting Rosanna from the care of the religious order at All Hallows', her home for sixty-six years, to some other institution. "Moorlands" had never been her home. James' reply to Duhig, written in the third person, was curt and final. With reference to Sister Mary Mel he "sees no reason to meet him and talk over her problems as he has no interest or control over her affairs." The Sisters of Mercy who continued to give her loving care were well rewarded; when Rosanna died in March 1934, her share of Patrick's estate passed to the Order. It consisted of valuable inner city land at the corner of Albert and Elizabeth Streets and the corner of Creek and Adelaide Streets; an allotment with a thirty-seven foot frontage to Edward Street; and a similar sized allotment fronting Adelaide Street. In suburbia there were two parcels of land totalling almost six acres at Mayne Junction, and eleven allotments at Ithaca. On the fast developing highway to Ipswich were thirty-two acres two roods which had been Patrick's stock-holding yard in the Gailes area. Its total value in 1892 was £39,964. Its value in 1996 was conservatively estimated to be $25,000,000.

By the mid-1930s nothing in the Maynes' life had changed except the onset of old age and its attendant weaknesses. The bursts of public applause in 1923 and 1926 had fizzled out, although there had been a minor splutter in 1930 when press photographs acknowledged the handing-over of the St Lucia site. The students toasted James' name in their "Varsity Students' Song" and the Arts students sang hopefully of soon being home on Dr Mayne's land. Such songs were part of a large repertoire, sung with gusto on happy occasions. Mayne was but one of many names they included.

Out in the wider world, people found it easy to forget those gifts which benefited the community and which James undoubtedly had hoped would restore their good name. Their life easily slipped back to being the property of gossips. In 1932, James leased a prime Queen Street site for fifty years to Capital Theatres so that they could build their ornate picture palace, The Regent. It showed the new "talkies" to an excited audience, but we do not know if the much maligned Maynes ever sought escape in that celluloid world. Their preferred leisure activity seemed to remain those private picnics to the Moggill land where James Pacey continued to farm — now as caretaker and tenant of the University. A car had replaced the carriage and James and his sister would sometimes drive to Sandgate to try to recapture dreams of youthful pleasure. The short time their mother had lived there with her children was the brightest jewel in James' memory. He spoke of it fondly and frequently. Those memories could only have glowed in his mind if his childhood relationship with his mother had been a loving one. We know she could be tough as steel when the occasion demanded; but the tough-tender, complex man who was James may have reflected a tenderness that was part of her character. One recorded trip was to Victoria Point to call on Dr Ernest Sandford Jackson, who had retired and thrown his energy into creating a large garden. In 1934 Jackson wrote of his pleasure when James and four ladies had called and enthused over his horticultural efforts. One of the ladies could have been Mary Emelia; the identity of the other three is unknown.

The University Senate, now committed to build at St Lucia, was making positive plans. Melville Haysom was commissioned to paint James' portrait. Presumably it was to be hung in some place of honour. As with William Jolly, the meeting with Haysom resulted in a friendship. Those who were prepared to look beyond the veil of gossip and take the trouble to get to know James found a genuine, likeable man. The life-sized portrait, brings out what Haysom saw in James during the sittings at his studio in Fortitude Valley. It shows an ageing, alert face with sparse white hair. The cleft chin and strongly marked brows over the blue eyes add to the strength of the face, but it is in those eyes and the gentle set of the mouth that Haysom has captured the caring essence of the man. The face gives no hint of the endless tragedy; the lips suggest humour which, in public, was probably never allowed free rein. It is the open face of a good man, someone you would like to know. Haysom painted James sitting in his black academic robes trimmed with white fur, and on his lap is a white plan titled: "Proposed University Site". At the top of the plan is his personal device, a winged heart over the words *sursum corda*.

An oft-told anecdote, which has a strong ring of truth, has it that the dominant J.D. Story, who, even before he became Vice Chancellor virtually ran the University, banished the portrait. Some say to a storeroom. It had been voted the most arresting picture in the 48th Annual Exhibition of the Royal Queensland Art Society; as a portrait it could hold its own with any on the campus. The reason for banishment must have been a rejection of the Maynes because of their reputation. James heard of the slight and sent a retainer to advise Mr Story that he was displeased. The retainer was forestalled by the Registrar, Mr Page-Hanify, who quietly had the portrait restored to its former place.

It was not to last. The painting again disappeared from

general view. With the University's restoration of the historic Customs House it was brought from obscurity at St Lucia and hung, untitled, unknown, and presumably unhonoured, in a small room on the top floor of that building. Perhaps the greatest indignity in that move was that the portrait was taken from the site which meant so much to James, the site he had given to the University, to be placed in a building which he would have avoided. It overlooks Kangaroo Point, where his father murdered Robert Cox. Patrick's act destroyed the reputation of his whole family. In giving the St Lucia site James could have hoped to live that down.

During the sittings for the portrait, James talked about his childhood at Sandgate. There was clearly an empathy between the two men and Haysom and his wife both enjoyed visits to "Moorlands". It was Melville who showed James one of the rare acts of kindness he received in his adult life. The thank you letter shows the warmth and easy grace of the recipient.

> Thank you for the beautiful painting of Sandgate, it was very good of you to do it for me. I will always appreciate the kindly thought as well as the very beautiful picture. As you know the memories of my childhood days at Sandgate are very dear to me, the best in my life in fact, though I have travelled round the world many times and seen all the best that was to be seen.
>
> So you will understand that nothing else could have given me such pleasure or touched more tender thoughts. *(11.7. 1936.)*

A year later, James heard that Haysom had shared a major prize in the State lottery, the Golden Casket, and won £1,000. His spontaneous letter to Mrs Haysom is an indication of the caring man:

> We just cannot imagine what your feelings are, as I just cannot describe my own on hearing the good news. I do not know of a family to whom I would rather the good luck had gone and certainly not a more worthy one. In the excitement this morning I forgot to thank Noel [their ten-year-old son] for the lovely flowers, please tell him for me that I appreciate his charming gift. The violets are extra specially good, and such a lovely perfume which leaves no doubt in my mind that they are Toowoomba violets. We are looking forward to seeing you again very soon and will be able to tell you in person of our great joy in your good fortune. *(12.8.1937.)*

That young son, Noel, now a retired scientist, still remembers James as the kindly, gentle man who sat for a portrait in his father's studio. He had not been jaundiced by parental prejudice and was able to know the delightful man who, elsewhere faced with a judgmental public, took refuge in a protective shell of indifference.

It is not surprising that with such a life, combined with the vulnerability of old age, James became somewhat eccentric. Where once his tolerance and understanding of human nature carried him through most difficult times, these were no longer his strengths. In old age, James was struggling to keep afloat in a sea of emptiness. Life was still a journey he had to make alone. Whisky helped. On occasions he was a lonely old man sitting in a state of refined intoxication; but he kept that under control. Mary Emelia, so long ago attractive and lively enough to be of concern to her brothers, was now overweight, sagging in face and figure, and sunk in apathy.

The family doctor for many years, the crusty, argumentative Sandford Jackson, now lived too far away at Victoria Point, so a series of doctors attended at "Moorlands". The eminent physician Dr Harry Windsor was summoned to attend for a time in 1936. He had no idea why he was chosen; a call came out of the blue. There was a set ritual. He had to telephone just before he went to "Moorlands", was met by the gardener at the gate, and the housekeeper at the front door. He was never taken into the house. He and James remained seated on the front veranda chatting about inconsequential things until it was time to leave. James' health was not good in those last years, but he almost never discussed it with the doctor.

One December day when the conversation lapsed, Dr Windsor mentioned the news that King Edward had just announced his abdication, and remarked that he could not understand why the King wanted to marry a divorced woman. Both men were Catholics and this was against their religious teaching. James' face became suffused with blood and he retorted, "You married men are always jealous of us bachelors." The next day he sent a message asking Dr Windsor not to visit any more. One or two other medical practitioners were sacked in the same abrupt manner.

The former Lord Mayor, William Jolly, now Federal Member for Lilley, called occasionally, but the only two people with whom James felt completely at ease were his agent, Waverley Cameron, and Fred Whitehouse who understood him and cared. Fred was now coach of the University rowing team. In 1937, when the Australian Universities' Eight Oar Race was to be held in Hobart, the Queensland crew had no suitable boat and insufficient money for the crew's competition expenses. The lack of such a boat was not unusual. The top secondary schools and the universities could afford fours, but to own an eight was to own a great treasure. Fred's request to James for help was met with £160 for a new boat and oars, with the money to ship it to Tasmania and a contribution towards the accommodation expenses of the coach and crew. Now seventy-six, James was a semi-invalid and not very sociable, but Fred took the crew to "Moorlands" to thank their donor. A manservant escorted the students upstairs to James' room where they were given refreshments in what turned out to be a very jolly hour. Dr Don Robertson, one of that year's crew, recalls that there was no sign of Mary Emelia, and that the ailing James had a large broad face, hanging jowls and not much hair.

The University boatshed was then at the Domain, near the city bend of the river at the George Street campus. After lectures, the crew usually rowed upstream in the evening light, and it was one of James' late-life pleasures to hear the swish of oars and watch the silhouette as they glided along the metal-dark water past "Moorlands". Fred, their coach, was always close behind in a sleek speedboat, an acquisition which was also thought to have been financed by James.

On Saturday 6 March 1937, James and Mary Emelia took their final public curtain: the laying of the University of Queensland's foundation stone at St Lucia. It was a bright sunny afternoon and both the ailing Maynes rose splendidly to the occasion. James was formal in silk top hat and morning suit with a white *boutonnière*, his large diamond pin flashing on his cravat, and a heavy gold chain anchoring his fob watch. His sister was encased in black, from the froth of ostrich feathers encircling her hat to the black lace coat fastened over her long black dress by her exquisite gold-and-diamond winged heart. It was the same Marian symbol that was carved into their staircase, on James' portrait and many of his belongings, and now apparently also cherished by Mary Emelia. She, too, wore white flowers and flourished her gold-and-diamond bracelet as they sat in state on a dais erected on the vast treeless hillside. Harrison Bryan recorded that the stone was laid by the Premier, W. Forgan Smith, with the encouragement of the Chancellor, the assistance of Mr J. Hennessy the architect, and the blessing of Dr J. O'Neil Mayne, the donor. The leading figures in the ceremony had celebrated rather too freely beforehand; Bryan notes that as a result, the proceedings were somewhat more spirited than had been expected.

It is commonly accepted that as a result of those high spirits the foundation stone was set in the wrong place and had to be shifted overnight. And there were those who remembered that as the area cleared of celebrants and staff, the stone was left isolated, pathetic and indistinguishable in the empty acres of grassland. The stone certainly was moved, but the official story is that it was due to a later decision to change the alignment of the Forgan Smith building.

Although the munificence of both the Maynes provided the land and they were guests of honour at the ceremony, their name does not appear among the many others on the foundation stone. The purist James may not have minded the omission, for the geologists on the staff at that time (among whom were Harrison Bryan's father and Dr Fred Whitehouse) did not approve of that first stone of what they hoped would be noble buildings. Harrison Bryan recalls, "it is an ersatz object produced by a company called Benedict Stone in which the Senate member, Archbishop Duhig, was known to have a considerable holding."

In his last years James was unable to walk the distance to St Lucia to enjoy the peace or dream of the University buildings which would rise there. He may have been too disheartened to care. The Government, burdened with loans, a deep economic depression, and a huge unemployed workforce, tightened its purse. The diehard opponents of St Lucia raised the site issue again. But theirs was a swan song. In March 1938, a year after the celebratory stone-laying, work began. James was now a very ill man, rarely leaving his room. He may never have seen the first fruits of his and Mary Emelia's generosity as the blocks of delicately coloured sandstone were shaped to form the first building. He would, however, have been kept informed of progress by Fred Whitehouse.

One warm January day, two weeks before he died, James asked to be taken to Sandgate so that he could have a last look at the beach resort where he had run barefoot as a boy. In his long troubled life that had been a rare and short time when he had been carefree and happy. They had great difficulty getting him into the car, but he insisted. He died on 31 January 1939.

As James had feared, a severely demented Mary Emelia survived him, but the two had made their plans as watertight as they could. Responsible to the end, he had been determined to leave the name of Mayne in high regard with the community. In December 1937 he had ensured they made identical wills, leaving everything to the University. James left £113,334 gross to the Medical School. When his sister died on 12 August 1940, her estate, which included their home "Moorlands" and a collection of costly furniture and family treasures, brought their joint benefit to the Medical Faculty to almost £200,000. The money was for equipment, to establish and maintain chairs of medicine and surgery, to endow medical research, and grant scholarships within the medical school.

Much of their income-bearing estate lay in city and suburban property. Some property, including the Brisbane

Arcade, which remains in the estate, continues to return an income. The enormous cedar dining-room suite at "Moorlands" became the Senate table and chairs, and the Steinway grand piano was used by the music students. Some furniture was later used in the Chancellor's robing room; the rest found its way into the offices of senior staff, most of whom appreciated their decorative treasures. Today, very little, if any of it, survives on campus. Similarly, "Moorlands" is no longer a University property. The Senate could find no use for it and overruled James' and Mary Emelia's expressed wish that it should remain part of the University. It was sold in 1944.

However, James would have approved the eventual use of his home and gardens as part of Wesley Hospital, serving the people. Yet he and his sister had been denied the intention behind that gift. Like the other benefactions, they hoped it would stand as a permanent reminder to the community that despite malicious gossip, all but two of the Mayne family were worthy, decent people. With the exception of Rosanna's share of her father's will, the entire Mayne fortune, held together and expanded by their mother, Mary, then further expanded by her four youngest children, passed to the University of Queensland.

In the 1860s, had anyone asked the wealthy businessman Patrick Mayne what he had inherited, he would have proudly answered, "Nothing. I'm a self-made man, my children will be the inheritors." They were, in every sense of the word. His genetic inheritance, potent and insidious, provided a legacy for his children which wrecked their lives mentally, morally and socially. No law exacted retribution from the criminals affected by that wilful gene, so freely handed on. That price was paid by the three youngest and innocent members of the family, persecuted by a vengeful public. Their memory remains besmirched today, almost sixty years after the death of the last member of the family. It is time their name was removed from the mire and given the place of honour which they deserve.

Epilogue

HOW strange is life? Patrick Mayne, one of Brisbane's first aldermen and a confessed murderer, is commemorated by Mayne Road and Mayne Junction, both at Mayne between the eastern suburbs of Bowen Hills and Albion. Just beyond Lang Park, on the western side of the city, two more streets carry his name, and a nearby street that of his unstable eldest son. They are Mayneview Street, Patrick Street and Isaac Street, all lying between Given Terrace and Milton Road, where Patrick had one of his many stock-holding yards and where his herdsman, Jacob Schelling, came to an untimely end. Both father and son are also remembered by superb stained-glass windows in St Stephen's Cathedral.

Although the last two innocent members of the Mayne

family died over fifty years ago and gave their large fortune to benefit the people of Queensland, where were their names honoured? Until recently the slate was almost blank.

Until now their name has never been cleared. Countless false, lurid stories of male rape and murder still exist. So common is the story of the Maynes' bizarre past that in 1975 the Taringa-based Popular Theatre Group sought details of the gory rumours in order to re-enact them as history. There is no evidence that the exercise ever got off the ground.

Over the years the force of the Maynes' unsavoury reputation appeared to pose a difficulty for the University of Queensland in the matter of adequately honouring them. In recent times it has been further exacerbated. There is a widespread current story that James made his fortune as Brisbane's chief abortionist. This, too, is a fabrication. Abortion is unlikely to have been much of a money-making practice in 1904, when James handed his resignation to the Hospital Board, nor would it in the early 1900s have made the sort of money the Maynes enjoyed. This story completely ignores the fact that as Resident Medical Officer and as Hospital Superintendent, James Mayne gave every penny of his salary to benefit the Brisbane General Hospital. In 1904 the responsible, humane James ceased to practise because he feared that if the family's genetic mental instability should manifest itself in him, he might harm someone. The hope that one day he might, with confidence, resume his career led him to keep current his medical registration. That day did not come; he never again used his professional skills.

Archbishop Duhig, who failed to gain a share of the fortune for the Church, nevertheless acknowledged the genuine, benign man who was the real James Mayne. In delivering the panegyric at St Stephen's Cathedral on 2 February 1939, he spoke of James as a noble and unselfish citizen who had given his professional services without monetary fee or reward, and whom he, personally, had known to perform many unpublished acts of kindness and generosity. On that occasion Mary Emelia, touched by Duhig's unexpected warmth, rewarded the Archbishop with £100.

It must never be forgotten that the Mayne gifts to the University of Queensland came from two people; James provided two-thirds and Mary Emelia one-third of the total. She was a very willing partner in the drawing-up of the identical wills. Nevertheless, she was not the initiator. It was James who conceived the idea of benefiting the people through the University. He did all the planning and with her agreement made the execution of his plan sufficiently watertight so that their estates still provide great annual wealth for the Medical School. Mary Emelia's diminished intellect and lack of interaction with the community made her easily forgotten as a benefactor — but James Mayne, the man whom the public knew and who continually spread largess, is almost equally neglected.

At the time of James' death, when his bequests were made known, the Chancellor of the University, Sir James

Blair, stated that James was the University's best friend. A spokesman for the University said: "The Senate will consider naming an outstanding section of the new university buildings after Dr Mayne" and added that they may place a life-sized portrait on the wall facing the entrance to the Great Hall, where all meetings would be held. Another stated: "James' monument is the University buildings at St Lucia."

These fine eulogic words were rapidly forgotten by all but two loyal friends, Dr Fred Whitehouse and William Jolly. During the following years both men voiced their anger and disappointment at the University's continued lack of recognition of the Maynes. There was nothing at the University to connect the name with the gift. The protests of the ageing William Jolly, no longer in politics, were of little avail. In 1954 Dr E. S. Meyers requested that recognition be given to the Maynes, and in 1959 the long-time Mayor of Brisbane, Sir John Chandler, added his public protest about the failure to honour them. University senators remained deaf.

In February 1969, thirty years after James' death, Dr Fred Whitehouse put angry pen to paper. He wrote to Convocation requesting that "the Senate of the University be asked to establish, within its precincts at St Lucia, a fitting memorial to the late Dr J. O'Neil Mayne and Miss Mayne". In his long, hard-hitting letter he also reminded the Senate that after the war the Committee of the Boat Club had decided to call the new boatshed the Mayne Boat Shed. When the Senate erected the new shed, without any reference to the Boat Club it was named the "Eric Freeman". Similarly, the Council of the Men Graduates Association of the University had proposed that some ornamental gates into the University grounds be erected as a memorial to Dr and Miss Mayne. This, too, was never done.

After a distinguished career at the University and an exceptionally distinguished military career in the Second World War, Associate Professor Whitehouse had unfortunately fallen foul of the law and had been dismissed from the University in November 1955. His protest on the Maynes' behalf appeared to have carried little weight. On the other hand, Whitehouse was a strategist. It is likely he was doing what he had done in *Galmahra* in 1927, raising a matter when there was a possibility of success.

Nine years earlier (1960) an appeal for funds had been launched to build the University a Great Hall. It had foundered for lack of support and the initial donors had seen nothing for their money. With the new Vice Chancellor, Professor Zelman Cowen at the helm, the project was revived and there was strong hope for the Hall's completion. Whitehouse's letter of protest was timely. In 1972, thirty-three years after the press was told that a building would be named after the Maynes, the new Hall was honoured by the name Mayne Hall. It is a most appropriate building to bear the name. Unfortunately, at all levels of the community it is generally thought to be the "Main" hall. Many buildings on the campus honour distinguished academics and carry the first and the family name of the person so honoured: Gordon Greenwood, Hartley Teakle, Zelman Cowen, J.D. Story and so on. With Mayne Hall, a simple change to James Mayne Hall would confirm that it is an honour name and prompt the question "Who was he?", thereby perpetuating a vital facet of the University's history.

Mayne Hall is an architectural statement and its wide expanse of glass does not easily lend itself to portraits or any other embellishment. In 1981, in an effort to mollify those who believed the Maynes were not sufficiently recognised, a small bronze plaque with the supposed profiles of James and Mary Emelia was placed in Mayne Hall. As with the excellent portrait of James until recently tucked away in the Customs House, it is far from view and recognition, placed high in a small, dimly lit seating bay on the far side of the entrance to the auditorium. Few have ever noticed it. In 1974, when the new Mayne Hall proved very suitable for concerts, a Mayne String Quartet featuring leading Brisbane musicians was formed. In 1980 it became the Mayne String Trio, but was disbanded in 1986. The honour name died with it.

At the Medical School at Herston, the large annual income from the Mayne Bequest continues to help make the Faculty a viable entity. Some of that money finances two professorial chairs, one for medicine and one for surgery. Each originally bore the name Mayne Professor but by the mid 1980s the name Mayne had been dropped from both.

Until now it has been true to say that at the University of Queensland and for some 160,000 men and women who, to date, have studied at the St Lucia campus, the name Mayne has little significance. The majority would never have heard of the family. Nor is there anything to tell the thousands of citizens who at weekends enjoy sport, long walks, or relaxing in the magnificent riverside grounds, who it was that provided what must be one of the most splendid university sites in Australia. James and Mary Emelia would have taken great pride in the way the campus has been developed. No one, it seemed, had the courage to be proud of them. 1995 saw some change in that. The Senate of the University resolved that James' and Mary Emelia's significant contribution to the Medical Faculty would be recognised by calling the School at Herston the Mayne Medical School. It was so named at a ceremony in December 1996. By April 2001 James' portrait, recently damaged, had still not been displayed in a place of honour for all to see on the St Lucia campus.

The University Library holds a sealed file, not to be opened before early in the twenty-first century. It is understood to contain the memoirs of several Brisbane medical men and may contain some material concerning James Mayne. It is to be hoped that those men who wrote for posterity personally knew their man, eschewed rumour and had a care for fact.

The false stories have been researched and shown to be what they are — cruel fabrications. It is a sad commentary on society that the good spread by James and Mary Emelia Mayne in their lifetime, which continues long after their deaths, took so long to be proudly proclaimed. The fact that some members of their family inherited a rogue gene and were driven by forces they could not control does not mean that the money donated by James and Mary Emelia Mayne is tainted. They gave to the University of Queensland its main campus at St Lucia, the large Veterinary Farm at Moggill, the valuable site of "Moorlands" and an income which by 1995 had grown to almost $1M a year to support the Faculty of Medicine.

James Mayne, the man who directed that generosity, should now be remembered by the words of William Jolly who spoke truly and sincerely when he said at James' funeral, "In him the community lost a good friend."

Sources

Abbreviations

ADB	*Australian Dictionary of Biography*
AO.NSW	Archives Office, New South Wales
BC	*Brisbane Courier*
MBC	*Moreton Bay Courier*
NSWGG	*New South Wales Government Gazette*
JOL	John Oxley Library
QGG	*Queensland Government Gazette*
QSA	Queensland State Archives
QSL	Queensland State Library
RCBAA	Roman Catholic Brisbane Archdiocesan Archives
UQA	University of Queensland Archives
UQFL	University of Queensland Fryer Library
UQP	University of Queensland Press

1. A Profitable Murder

The Cox murder: Archives Office, New South Wales, 9/6345 Supreme Court, Brisbane, Regina vs William Fyfe. 1848. Cedar Cutting: AO, NSW. 4/1099.2 Colonial Secretary Misc., Special Bundles.

2. Ireland to Australia

For immigration and the early years of Patrick Mayne and Mary McIntosh see AO, NSW, Bounty Index 28–42, rolls 1336 and 1343, Assisted Immigration Archives. For Kangaroo Point in C19th I have drawn on Brisbane History Group Papers No 6, "People, Places and Pageantry" 1987 and W. Ross Johnston, *Brisbane — The First Thirty Years* (Brisbane: Boolarong Publications, 1988). For a history of the slaughterhouse I read John Greig Smith's "The Foundation of Kangaroo Point" in "People, Places and Pageantry"; *Moreton Bay Courier*, various issues April 1848–October 1849; Queensland State Archives, CPS. Bench of Magistrates 1846. All land transactions were searched in NSW and Qld *Government Gazettes*; Qld Lands Office Register of Land Sales; QSA, Land Transfers, and the Immigration Register of Land Orders. For petty crime I consulted QSA, files and *MBC*, various issues. For Hotel Licenses see QSA, CPS Moreton Bay Record of Recognisances 1848–. Information on the McGrath and Pacey families came from a 1994 interview with a descendant, Mrs Kay Bothwell.

3. Law Courts and Land Deals

Much of Patrick's life was traced through advertisements, public notices and court cases reported in the *MBC*; Queensland State Library, Colonial Secretary's Letters; and QSA, Brisbane General Hospital file 1852; SCT/P7 Eccles.298, 1865, Mayne Estate accounts; QSA/TRE 15 Rosevale Station. The Thomas

Dowse property sale was noted in Johnston, *Brisbane — The First Thirty Years*, p. 123. Material on Dara is from N.J. Byrne, *Robert Dunne: Archbishop of Brisbane 1830–1917* (St Lucia: UQP, 1991), p.71 and the Roman Catholic Brisbane Archdiocesan Archives.

4. Consolidating an Empire

For petitions and charitable funds see QSL, Colonial Secretary's Letters, 1853–1854 and *MBC*, various issues. For Jacob Schelling's death see *MBC*, 10.2.1858. Western Creek is now the Milton drain. The waterhole was in the vicinity of Lang Park. QSA hold Patrick's will, SCT/P7 Eccles. 298, 1865 and the Darragh divorce papers, QSA, SCT/CH 6, No. 85. Demolition of Dara is described in T.P. Boland, *James Duhig* (St Lucia: UQP, 1986), p. 37. Material on the first town Council came from Brisbane Council Archives and G. Greenwood and J. Laverty, *Brisbane 1859–1959. A History of Local Government* (Brisbane City Council, 1959).

5. In and Out of Council

John Cameron's reminiscences are at the Oxley Memorial Library. The Queen Street fire was reported in the *Brisbane Courier* 12.4.1846.

6. Life in Queen Street 1860–1865

W.R.O. Hill's anecdote is in his *45 Year's Experience in North Queensland 1861–1905* (Brisbane: H Pole & Co., 1907). For Bishop Quinn's immigration scheme see *Australian Dictionary of Biography*, 1851–1890, vol. 5, H.J. Gibbney, "James Quinn"; and QSA, Assisted Immigration files. Information on Father Dunne is drawn from Byrne, *Robert Dunne*. I obtained material on Rosanna Mayne at a 1993 interview with the late Sr Jean

Marie at All Hallows' Convent, and drew on Sr Mary Xaverious, *Beyond Our Dreams* (Brisbane: Jacaranda Press, 1961) and Byrne, *Robert Dunne*. The second Queen Street fire was reported in the *BC*, 2.12.1864.

7. Crisis After Crisis

For the Qld Steam Navigation Co., see Denis Cryle, *The Press in Colonial Queensland* (St Lucia: UQP, 1989) and *MBC*, various issues. Extra background material on Archbishop Dunne comes from his Letter Book held in microfilm at the QSL. Reference to the Cox murder is in Henry Stuart Russell, *The Genesis of Queensland* (NSW: Turner and Henderson, 1888), p. 395 and J.J. Knight, *In the Early Days* (Brisbane: Sapsford and Co., 1895), pp. 237–244. The Irish anecdote about horses at a murderer's funeral came from Mr Ed Mulroy, grandson of a witness at the funeral. It is also noted by Gwen Harwood, *Blessed City* (Angus & Robertson, 1990), p. 210. A 1993 interview with the late Mrs Thelma McConnell revealed that news of hereditary insanity in the Mayne family was given to the McConnells by Dr Lilian Cooper. For Mary Mayne's difficulties with her husband's debt, see QSA., Queensland Supreme Court, Equity Jurisdiction 4.11.1868 and Z55, SCT, Eccles. 289. Also *QGG.*, Nov. 1869, Dec. 1879. Bishop Quinn's debts are noted by Byrne, p. 64.

8. Out of the Ashes

The Mooney family information provided by Mr Barry Alexander in 1994 is held at RCBAA. Mary Mayne's life is compiled from family documents held at QSA; *Shaw's Brisbane Directory and Squatters' Guide, 1876*; OML, S.W. Jack's Cutting Book No 11; *BC*, Shipping Lists 29.3.1878. For Rosanna's life I have drawn on N.J. Byrne, Sr Mary Xaverious, Sr Jean Marie, and the All Hallows' Convent Archivist. (See Sources Ch.6). For the boys' education I drew on the Estate accounts; Brisbane Grammar School Archives; RCBAA, St Killian's School file; and records at the University of Sydney. Isaac's legal training: QSA, SCT/CK11 and CK 12. The Markwell family information came from QSL, Grave Inscriptions and *BC*, 15.10.1868. It should be noted that Patrick Mayne was in Brisbane when Fyfe was executed and did not witness it as stated by H.S. Russell.

9. A Family Ostracised

For Isaac's involvement with Mrs Kelly's will see QSA, Z155, Eccles. I learned of the *Walrus* rumours from Mrs Libby Wager of Kenmore. The *Walrus*' history is in Ronald Parsons, *Paddle Steamers of Australasia* (Lobethal, South Australia: R. Parsons, 1973). James qualified MRCS.,LRCP.,London University, 1890. For his association with Brisbane General Hospital see QSA.Hos 1, BGH. Minutes. M'ship of various societies is noted in *Pugh's Almanac*, 1891–1903. For the family's travel to Europe refer AO.NSW, Outward Bound X489,490, 1903. Information on homosexual activity in Brisbane came from Dr Clive Moore, "The Abominable Crime: First Steps Towards a Social History of Male Homosexuals in Colonial Queensland, 1859–1900" in *Gay Perspectives II*, ed. Robert Aldrich (Sydney: University of Sydney, 1993). Florence Davidson's diary came from her granddaughter, Mrs Jill Bruxner.

10. The Tobita Murder and its Aftermath

The Tatsuzo Tobita papers are at QSA, Jus/N.180. 1904. The death was reported in *BC*, 10.6.1904. For James' handling of Isaac's illness see AO.NSW, R5/5885 Register of Patients and Admissions Book, Casebook No. 6, and R5/5881 Register of Discharges, Removals and Deaths. For the death of Carl

Markwell, see QSA, Jus/N 58, 1905. Rosanna's deed of assignment is held with Isaac's estate papers, QSA, Z1701, 294, 1905.

11. The Burden of Inheritance

I was told of the Moggill residents' regard for James and Mary Emelia by Mrs Libby Wager. Material on Dr E.S. Jackson came from N. Parker and J. Pearn, eds, *Ernest Sandford Jackson*, (The Australian Medical Asscn (Qld Branch) and the Dept Child Health, University of Queensland, 1987), with particular reference to the chapters by Dr Clarence Leggett and Dr Geoffrey Kenny. For James' interest in rowing see *Pugh's Almanac*, various years. For his association with Dr Fred Whitehouse I drew on the University of Queensland Archives, S130, 56800/70250/01 Memorials Mayne, 1969. William's will is held at QSA, SCT, Eccles.699, 1921. James Mayne's relations with Archbishop Duhig are noted in Boland, *Duhig*, especially p. 233. Additional material came from an interview with Mr Norman Jolly son of the former Mayor of Brisbane, William Jolly. For details of the Maynes' major gifts of land, refer UQ Archives, and M. Thomis, *A Place of Light & Learning* (St Lucia: UQP, 1985). The article on the Brisbane Arcade is published in *A & B Journal of Queensland*, 7.11.1923; 7.2.1924.

12. Maynes and the University of Queensland

The debates over the sites are covered in Thomis, *A Place of Light & Learning*. The gift of the site is recorded in W.A. Jolly, *The Inauguration of Greater Brisbane* (held OML); various issues of the *BC* and *Brisbane Telegraph*, October 1926; Harrison Bryan, "The University of Queensland 1910–1960, an Essay Towards a History" (held UQFL). For Dr Whitehouse's comments see UQFL, *Galmahra*, April 1927. Archbishop Duhig's effort to build the Holy Name Cathedral is covered in Boland's

Duhig. With reference to the Archbishop's financial difficulties, Boland notes (p.243) that he approached the Works Minister, Mr Sizer, with a plan to supply masses of Benedict stone for the University buildings. For James' refusal to accept the care of Rosanna, refer RCBAA, James Mayne to James Duhig, 4.1.1930. The schedule of Rosanna's land was provided by the Srs of Mercy, Brisbane Congregational Archives. James' letters to the Haysoms are held UQFL. Dr Morgan Windsor provided the anecdote of his father's association with James Mayne.